The Dreamers

Joy Haney

The Dreamers by Joy Haney
© 1994, Radiant Life Publications

Printed in the United States of America.
Library of Congress Catalog Number 94-068661
ISBN 1-880969-04-1

TABLE OF CONTENTS

PREFACE

*T*his book is written to dreamers who refuse to settle for mediocrity, who are not afraid to take a dare, or those who desire to conquer their fears. It is for the success-conscious, or for anyone that has the potential to become the Abraham Lincolns and the Thomas Edisons. This book is for the diligent and brave who would look into the stars and see God, those who would scan the universe and dream with it instead of being intimidated by it. *The Dreamers* will awaken within you new vision and help your dream stay alive. The curse of mankind is that many die with their dream still within them; even while living, they opt for the mundane or a life of drudgery. This book will help kindle or rekindle your dream and preserve you from letting your dream die!

The quality of life is closely related to the attitudes of the mind. How people think with their minds determines how they live or how they view the world around them. Ancient King Solomon wrote that actions are determined by the thinking process.

Your mind is like Grandma's old trunk in the attic, filled with all sorts of things that represent an experience of the past. It stores information in the form of lace, albums, books, wedding dresses, etc. Likewise, your mind is a storehouse. You can make it a treasure chest or a garbage can. To win, excel, and succeed you must guard what is allowed to be stored in your mind.

This book is filled with treasures from the past, principles that work, and concepts that have stood firm for centuries. The wisdom of the ages and truth from the sages is brought to life in the following fictional story: Jonathan, the main character, is joined by four other young men who all arrive at a School of Dreamers quite by accident. They, being filled with discouragement and loneliness, are ready to give up their dreams. Together they find new vigor, life, and excitement; their dreams are renewed as they study historical facts, truth and actual experiences of great men and women.

Read this book with a highlighter, pen and notebook. It is a life-changing book that will whisper hope to your heart and excite you once again. You *can* excel, dream and do in spite of difficulties, prejudices, and apparent impossibilities in life!

1

THE CRASH AND THE DREAM

Chilling fear in the pit of his stomach was all the young man could feel as he hurtled down the mountain. In his ears he heard the sound of metal crunching and saw only tree branches flying by, and then he felt a sudden jolt and stillness.

He woke up thinking, "Where am I?" as he lay prostrate on his back staring through the towering evergreen trees. Then he remembered, "I was driving down the mountain road, feeling so despondent, when the brakes of my car went out."

His body ached and his mind was in a fog. Sensing he was not alone, his eyes slowly searched the surrounding area when he saw a man looking at him with piercing eyes. He felt a tremor of fear go through his bruised and somewhat battered body, not knowing the intentions of the man and from where he came.

Kindly the man said in a low strong voice, "You are hurt. Let me help you."

The tall older man continued to talk as he walked towards the younger man. "You probably don't know where you are, but no one comes here without being recommended by somebody," he stated matter-of-factly.

The young man, looking puzzled, said, "I'm not sure where I am, but I do remember crashing down the mountain and this must be where I landed."

"Yes," joined in the man, "you came down the mountain in quite a hurry. We checked your car and you had shifted into low gear which helped soften the impact of the crash tremendously."

"I'm thankful for that, but how did you get here, and what is this place?" asked the young man whose body was starting to shake from the shock of the accident.

The gray-headed man smiled reassuringly as he answered while pointing with his finger towards some low white buildings in the distance. "I live over there," he said. "This is a school for true dreamers. People come here to learn how to realize their dreams, spending two weeks acquiring a new lesson each day, and at the end of that time they have treasures from the past to take with them. Only special people are allowed. We do not waste our time on wishers, we spend our time only helping dreamers, for often dreamers not only dream, they reach their dreams."

The young man whispered to himself, "I had a dream once, but it seemed so far away."

The sharp ears of the older man picked up the words that the younger man had spoken. He sensed the despondency of the young man and responded with these words: "The glow of a dream and an inspiration warms man. The dream can be as fresh today as when it was first created in the brain. The mind can seize it again and cause it to become larger, more powerful than before. You are not the first person to feel hopeless. History is full of people who faced closed doors and insurmountable odds. In the face of adversity, when all seemed against him, Christopher Columbus setting out to discover a new route to the Orient wrote these immortal words: 'This day we sailed on.' "As the voyage droned on and on he came to write them not once, but many times in his diary. Many years later Joaquin Miller read the words that had been inserted day after day, and penned a poem entitled *Columbus*. The fourth stanza of that poem thunders at the world today:

> 'What shall we do when hope is gone?'
> The words leapt like a leaping sword:
> 'Sail on! Sail on! Sail on! Sail on!'[1]

"That is what you are to do. Sail on towards your dream in the midst of the sea of life." Then he paused, looking kindly at the young man lying on the ground covered with pine needles, and said, "Here I am philosophizing while you are in pain. There's not much blood, but maybe some broken bones. Let's check and see."

Gently the older man checked the young man's arms, legs, and back, which remarkably had sustained no breaks. He then helped him get up while placing the young man's arm over his shoulder.

As they started to walk, the older man said, "You will come with me and rest the remainder of the day, but first I will tend to your bruises, give you some broth, and then you will feel better."

His benefactor led him to an all-white building which contrasted sharply against the dark greens and browns of the forest. Arriving there the man unlocked the door and placed his patient upon a very welcomed bed.

Sounds of running water and cabinets opening filled the stillness of the room. As the older man came back into the room he held in his hand a steaming bowl of hot water, some soft cloths, and an antiseptic. Competently he washed the bruises and scratches of the young man, making him feel very cared for and comfortable. He also helped remove his torn clothing, substituting them for soft flannel pajamas that were kept in the drawer of an old oak dresser. As he worked over the young man, he said, "By the way, my name is Benjamin. What is your name?"

"My name is Jonathan," the young man responded sleepily. Closing his eyes he started drifting off into a deep sleep as Benjamin finished caring for his needs.

While asleep the dream came to him. There appeared an old man wearing the robes of a king who was walking in his garden and talking to a young man. The king spoke and said, "A dream in its infancy is a very private thing. It is born in a moment of inspiration." Then the king pointed his finger at the young man and tapped him on the chest, saying, "Your dream is still private, for you have not reached it yet. This past year you were discouraged and wanted to give up your dream. You thought, 'What am I among so many?'" Then, lifting his finger and waving it in the air, he spoke these words: "All the rivers run into the sea, yet the sea is not full. There is always room for your dream to be fulfilled in the sea of life. Your dream is like a river. It starts small as a rivulet, but that rivulet gets bigger and bigger on its way to the sea. A small thought comes unexpectedly and increases daily in your mind. An idea is nurtured and a flash of inspiration weaves itself into the brain until it becomes so full it bursts into an ocean of influence."

The king stopped talking while peering closely into the young man's face and then the dream started fading as he spoke these final words: "Dream again! You can become or do something that will make the world a better place to live. Failure once does not constitute finality. All conquerors failed more than once. Your dream can be realized, but you must work hard at it."

Then the young man slept the exhausted sleep of one who has had a great shock.

2

THE PRESIDENT

Sirens, excited voices and revved-up motors awakened Jonathan from his deep sleep. As he started to get up, sharp muscular pains shot through his body. Then he remembered the crash, the old man and the unique School for Dreamers. Slowly lying back down he heard running footsteps coming toward his cottage. There was a quick knock and then the door opened. There stood Benjamin who had helped him the night before.

His facial expression showed agitated excitement. He said, "We've had another crash today, but it was not an automobile. It was a small plane."

Jonathan asked anxiously, "Is anybody hurt?"

"We got the young man out," Benjamin answered, "and it does not look like he is badly hurt, just some broken bones and a few cuts."

"If I appear overly excited," Benjamin continued, "it is because this has been a very unusual week. This is the fifth boy who has come to us and all of them were hurt or lost.

"Monday, one of the guides from the school found two boys panting on the riverbank thoroughly soaked who had been nearly drowned. In their harrowing escape from the tempestuous river they lost their canoe and all their gear. After bringing them to the school's doctor it was discovered that one of the boys was going through withdrawals.

"Then," Benjamin continued, "another boy stumbled into our place half-starved. He had been lost for several days and could not find his way out. Now he is resting and building his strength. Yesterday, you crashed here and now today the fifth boy has landed here."

Jonathan asked in puzzled tones, "What are you going to do with all of us?"

Benjamin spoke with repressed excitement, "The President of the school has been meeting with the teachers and has decided to open the school for two weeks for you five while you rest and recuperate."

"Why would he do that?" Jonathan asked.

Benjamin looked through the window toward the mountains and said, "The President is an unusual man who cares deeply for the youth of this generation. He feels if he can help one, maybe that one will help thousands. His philosophy is that we all touch the lives of other people, and some more than others. He says it is a strange coincidence that brought five young men to us within one week, and all of them were struggling with life. He feels like this school could give them the direction they are seeking and help propel them toward realizing their dream in life."

Jonathan answered slowly, "I have not met many people like the President. He must be a great man, but have you talked with the other four young men about this?"

"Oh, yes," Benjamin responded, "all except the young man that was brought here this morning. The other three are rather excited about the idea. They were on vacation anyway, so now they will live here for two weeks in these cottages and gain new inspiration while having fun."

"Well," Jonathan answered thoughtfully, "maybe that is what I need. My car must be totally wrecked, so I am stranded."

"Surprisingly, it is not as bad as one would expect. It is salvageable, so we've already taken your car to a nearby body shop," Benjamin responded. "They said they could have it ready in about two weeks."

"Good," Jonathan answered, feeling relieved. Filled with all kinds of questions he asked, "When do the lessons start, how much does it cost, and where are the classrooms?"

Benjamin held up his hand. "Wait a minute," he said, speaking in authoritative tones. "The classes will begin tomorrow. Your meals will be provided, and the President is waiving the fee it normally would cost. You will be taken to your classroom every day and given materials to study. At the end of two weeks you will face real life again, but this time you will be better equipped to handle it."

Turning to go but talking all the while, Benjamin said, "Your breakfast will be brought to you, and later today you might want to meet the others in the dining hall for an early dinner."

As Benjamin walked out the door a drowsy peace settled upon Jonathan and he fell asleep again. About an hour later the knock on the door awakened him and he hollered, "Come in!"

Benjamin walked in with a tray full of breakfast food, exiting as quickly as he came, saying he would be back in the afternoon. After eating the delicious breakfast Jonathan walked slowly around the room, flexing his muscles as the soreness washed over him like a sludge-filled river. While he paused before a window and gazed at the beauty of the mountains, feelings welled up within him that shaped themselves into words: "I couldn't have chosen a better spot if I would have tried."

After walking around some more he stretched himself across the bed, groaning with the sheer pleasure of being able to rest his aching muscles. All was quiet once more and the quietness rocked him gently to sleep again. Later that day it took several minutes of pounding on the door to awaken him from an exhausted sleep.

Groggily he answered, "Come in," while the only man he had seen since the crash walked in holding something in his hand.

Benjamin's words were quick and to the point. "It is 3:30 and dinner is served at 4:30. Do you think you feel well enough to go to the dining hall?"

Jonathan shook his head, rubbed sleep from his eyes and answered, "I'll be there, just tell me how to get there."

Benjamin handed him a map with a red line showing the way. "This will take you right there," he said smiling. Then placing a package in Jonathan's hand, he said, "Here are your clothes which have been mended and cleaned. Later you can go to the lost and found and pick some more out for you. Through the years we have built quite a collection of things left by the different people that have come and gone."

As Benjamin left and closed the door behind him, Jonathan started feeling a little nervous about meeting new people. He dressed slowly while thinking about the future, and then hesitantly walked outside. Seeing no one he followed the red lines which led him to the dining hall. Rather fearfully he opened the door and saw only seven people seated around a table. Benjamin happened to glance his way, jumped up, came over to the door and led him to where they were all sitting.

Pointing to Jonathan he introduced him to those sitting down, saying, "This is Jonathan, the one that crashed yesterday." Then further introductions were made. There was John, the boy who had been lost; Tim and Michael, the two who had lost their canoe and almost drowned; two of the teachers, Miss Elizabeth and Mr. Warner, and then when Benjamin came to the sixth person he showed great respect and honor as he said, "This is our President, Mr. Theodore."

Everyone made Jonathan feel welcome and as he sat down to eat with them there was a camaraderie among them. He noticed when the President spoke that everyone hung on to his every word. He started talking about his father. He said, "My father was a man of the earth. He worked hard all his life and he expected us to do likewise. His favorite saying was, 'He who knows how to work has laid the cornerstone of success, and he who knows how to economize has raised his own wages.'

"He used to lead the family in prayer and taught us that God helps those who help themselves. He used to say, 'God has great plans for every life. A friendship with Him will be the realization of those plans.' Yes, Father taught us that courage, dignity, responsibility and hard work would help anyone succeed."

The President continued talking while everyone listened carefully. "When I would want to sit doing nothing, my father would come by and say, 'Theodore, too much idleness is not good. Life is a journey, and should be upward, which means struggle. Now get to work!'"

Jonathan glanced around the circle of people at the table and wondered if they were feeling like he was. He could not help but feel that the President was a man of steel, for he exuded confidence and power, and did not seem to be afraid of anything.

His thoughts were interrupted by the President's voice. "Young men, you will find there are no drugs, tobacco products, alcoholic beverages, or hard rock music here. Why? Because I have discovered these things help destroy instead of build the mind."

Soon after, Benjamin took Jonathan and the other three young men over to the doctor's quarters. He asked the doctor if they could see the young man who had crashed in the plane that morning. As the doctor ushered them in, there lay a blond-headed, cheerful young man.

He spoke first. "Am I ever glad to be alive. I only have some cuts and a fractured left arm. Was I ever lucky," he said.

Benjamin said, "Great. Then you will be able to start lessons with us tomorrow."

"Oh, yes, the President has already told me about this school," he said. "The strange thing is, I was just about to give up on an invention I've been working on and just get a nine-to-five job doing something I didn't want to do. After talking to the President I already feel renewed hope. That guy oozes with strength and confidence. I know I'm going to like it here."

Benjamin introduced everyone all around. Jonathan found out that the name of the talkative patient was Joe.

Later that night, while getting ready for bed in his cottage, Jonathan felt as if he had been thrust into an unreal setting, almost like Alice in Wonderland. It was new, exciting and scary. Thoughts tumbled over themselves as he drifted off to sleep.

3

LIVE DELIBERATELY

*T*he next morning, bright sunlight shone through the window with such intensity that the glare of the sun forced Jonathan's eyes to open. He awakened to a stillness found only deep in the mountains covered with towering scented pine trees. Sitting up in bed, his eyes fell on the large clock Benjamin had brought the night before. He found it hard to believe that he had slept until 9:00 a.m.

There came a light tap at the door and knowing who it was he said, "Come in." Benjamin walked in with a tray of breakfast food, placing it on the round oak table, saying, "Now tomorrow, breakfast will be served in the dining hall. You will eat all your meals there during the remainder of your stay." He paused and looked at Jonathan, asking, "How are you feeling?"

"My body is a little stiff, but I am feeling much better today," he answered.

"Remember," said Benjamin, "School begins at 10:00. I am your guide while you are here and I will be back at 10:00 to take you to the place of inspiration today. Oh, yes, a word about your lesson today. It will be a brief time of introduction.

Each day the lessons will not be lengthy, but they will be effective. You will have assignments and material to study, then time to meditate, explore, and think."

As he opened the door to go outside, his last words were, "Be ready."

Promptly at 10:00 Benjamin came for Jonathan. It seemed they were alone in the forest. As they walked toward their destination, Jonathan asked, "Are there usually very many people here? Where is everyone?"

Benjamin answered slowly, "There was a time when there were more here, but now the number has dwindled to about a thousand that pass through these doors each year. It seems there are not as many dedicated dreamers as there used to be. Oh, there's the wishers and talkers, but few who just never give up and win. The reason why there is no one here except you five is because the school has been closed down for a two-month rest."

Impressed, Jonathan said, "To think that the President opened the school especially just for me and the others!"

With a half-smile on his face, Benjamin kiddingly responded, "We figured anybody who made such a grand entrance such as you must be a pretty serious dreamer. When you crashed you mentioned your dream, so we decided to open just for you, and of course, the other four."

As Jonathan followed Benjamin into a small room he thought, "My dream that had become tarnished, and had caused me disillusionment, has somehow brought me to this moment in time."

As Benjamin left, Jonathan waved good-bye and greeted the other four young men who were to be his classmates for the next two weeks. Sitting down near a window, he noticed at the front of the room a short bald-headed man bursting with enthusiasm and who seemed to have a lighted bulb inside him. He introduced himself and began talking like a machine gun as he handed John some stiff papers to give to each of them.

"These go in the notebook that is on each of your desks. This first lesson is a brief summary of ideas that need to be considered before anyone is able to reach his dream. They are entitled, *How to Master, Conquer, and Win.*"

The teacher then began to expound upon the following points:

1. **Achievement**—Always seek to reach the highest level of achievement you are able to attain. Never settle for second best or mediocrity. Be consistent and persistent until you reach your goal.

2. **Attitude**—Seek to cultivate the wonder of a child. Be curious, not jaded, but filled with excitement, laughter and the ability to enjoy the present with no pretense. Instead of focusing on the dirty window, see the sun shining through it. Be a winner! Defeat is an inner feeling. Free yourself from self-defeating attitudes.

3. **Commitment** is needful to win. Uncommitted people faint when the going gets rough. Everyone will encounter difficulties and discouraging moments but winners have the attitude, "Live, die, sink, or swim, I am going to win!"

4. **Create**—Once in awhile become so immersed in a project that you forget to look at the clock. Let the glow of excitement and creativity pulsate through your brain. Do not become dull because of constant work that is only an obligation, but do something that lets you be creative. Stay alive! You were meant to soar, invent and be inspired.

5. **Distractions**—Rid yourself from conflicting passions that bid for your valuable possession of time. Do not muse or meditate on them. Give your thoughts to that which is most important!

6. **Forgiveness**—Do not blame people in the past who did you wrong. These feelings only erect gates to fence you out and keep you from finding happiness and fulfillment. Forgive and get the poison out of your system.

7. **Giving**—Give to others. Let the glow that comes from enriching another's life warm you. Anywhere you stand you can always warm another soul. Give a smile, a kindness, a listening ear, or some encouragement. Do not be artificial, be real. Leave the seat of the judges; join the merciful. Do not waste time on being critical or tearing others down. This is wasted emotion. Move ahead!

8. **Gratitude**—Learn to be thankful, for this is an art to be learned. Grabbers never win in the end. It is the small courtesy that is rewarded. Show your appreciation by a single rose, a phone call, a note or a smile. You will be reciprocated richly.

9. **Hope**—Look at the possibilities instead of the impossibilities. Seize the moment. Always work toward the goal. Do not give into despair.

10. **Purpose**—It is your guiding star. Learn to master the negative things instead of letting them master you, for whatever you do not master will become your master. Purpose to do, and then do it.

11. **Soar**—Do not be chained to the treadmill of frustration. You can curse the darkness or light a candle. Live without anxiety and fretfulness by organizing your life. Change if you need to, but fly instead of sagging.

12. **Thoughts**—Do not be an ordinary thinker. Delve into the wisdom of old. Resist mental suicide. If you have lost zest and seethe with resentment and anger, you are slowly dying. Work every day at changing your thoughts from defeat to victory. Will yourself to think positive!

13. **Win**—Have a winning attitude inside of you, for that is where winning begins. See yourself winning before you win. You have to believe you can do it.

14. **Live Deliberately**—Deliberate much before you say or do anything for it will not be in your power to recall what is said or done. Whatever is written in cement should be written with purpose and not with a spur-of-the-moment pen. Live life to the fullest—do not waste it, but live deep and purposefully.

The teacher paused and then said, "Now, please, open the book on your desk and read the essay by Thoreau entitled *Walden*. Notice especially page 81, the paragraph that begins with, 'I wished to live deliberately...and not, when I came to die, discover that I had not lived. I did not wish to live what was not life, living is so dear. I wanted to live deep and suck out all the marrow of life. Why should we live with such hurry and waste of life?'"[1]

The teacher then left the five young men with some reading material and bid them good-day. After doing the reading assignment and discussing the lesson with each other, they walked out of the classroom into the brilliant sunshine. Jonathan sat down under a tree on a log bench and reflected upon all he had learned, while the others went to their cottages.

Later in the day they all met again in the dining room where they enjoyed a delicious dinner. Jonathan's eyes moved around the room searching for the President, but he was not there, so he invited his four new friends to go on a nature trail close to the camp area.

ॐঔ

Much later as he was getting ready for bed, his thoughts were racing with all that he had heard and experienced that day. When he climbed into bed and turned out the light, his last thoughts were about living deliberately. He determined to get a hold of life and squeeze all the marrow out of it, since much of his time in the past had been wasted.

4

NEVER GIVE UP!

*T*he next morning when Jonathan awoke, a gray cloud hung over the grounds. As he dressed for the day, a gray feeling settled over his emotions. Yesterday was so inspirational; this morning was so blah! He thought, "This emotional roller coaster inside of me is revolting. There has to be a better way."

Later after breakfast, when Benjamin came to get him, Benjamin noticed Jonathan's expression and his keen eye noticed that something was amiss.

"What's wrong?" he asked with concern.

"Oh, I don't know. I wish someone would explain it to me. Last night excitement surged through me; today I feel awful."

"Aha!" Benjamin said, "Today's lesson is just what you need."

As they left the cottage Jonathan followed Benjamin to the location where the lesson would take place. He noticed a ramp leading up to the door. When going inside, he knew why. The teacher was in a wheelchair.

The woman who sat in the chair smiled gently at the five young men who were finding places to sit and said, "Good morning" as if she really meant it. "You are going to like today's lesson. It is interesting and challenging."

As Jonathan looked at her face, a force emanated from her such as he had never seen. This woman had struggled, but had made it; she was an achiever. She pulled a picture down and started talking about the twenty-sixth President of the United States. The five listened as her voice opened new worlds to them.

"Little Teddy Roosevelt was born in New York City, October 27, 1858. He had great energy, curiosity, and determination, but he was puny and often ill. He suffered greatly from asthma and it was also discovered that he was near-sighted. When he was thirteen years old, while on a trip to Maine, he was tormented by two mischievous boys. He felt ashamed because he was not able to fight back.

"Because of this incident in his life, his father built him a gym in the family home and Theodore worked consistently trying to build up his puny under-developed body. He worked untiringly, until finally the day arrived that he overcame his asthma and built up unusual physical strength. Now, instead of boys wanting to torment a frail pushover, they looked at him with new respect and did everything in their power to stay in his favor.

"The same never-give-up attitude that characterized those pain-filled years was with him again on February 14, 1884, at the age of 26. On Valentine's Day, his wife of four years died while giving birth to their daughter. On the very same day his mother died of typhoid fever. He lost the two best friends he ever had on the exact same day. How can someone survive such heartaches?

"His heartbreak caused him to leave politics for a short time. 'He bought two cattle ranches on the Little Missouri River in the Dakota territory. The hard life and endless activity of a rancher helped him recover from his sorrow. Wearing cowboy clothes, Roosevelt often spent fourteen to sixteen hours a day in the saddle. He hunted buffalo and other wild animals and even helped law officers capture a band of outlaws.'[1]

"During this time the wild winds dried the tears that would fall unbidden down his cheeks. In the evening he worked on and completed two books: a biography of Senator Thomas Hart Benton of Missouri and *The Winning of the West*. In the winter of 1885-86, he had another major mishap. The severe snowstorms destroyed most of his cattle. After losing his investment, he returned to New York City in 1886 and, at the request of Republican leaders, ran for mayor. He was badly defeated.

"This young man who had many defeats, deaths, failures, and heartbreaks finally became Vice President of the United States of America in 1900. On September 6, 1901, President McKinley was shot by an assassin, and eight days later Theodore Roosevelt became President of the United States.

"His down times never dominated him for long. He always rose again. He never gave up. His character was revealed again on October 14, 1912. A saloon keeper named John N. Schrank tried to assassinate Roosevelt. Shrank shot Roosevelt just before he made a speech in Milwaukee. An eyeglasses case in Roosevelt's pocket deflected the bullet and probably saved his life. Even with the bullet in his chest, Roosevelt insisted on making his speech. He recovered from the wound in about two weeks.

"Normal people, when they get shot, take care of the wound as soon as possible. This bulldog of a man stood and gave his speech, then went to the doctor. His life was characterized by the words, NEVER GIVE UP! All things that are accomplished cannot be achieved without these three words."

As the teacher paused to take a drink, Jonathan sat there with inspiration again rising in his brain. He looked around at the other four and wondered if they were experiencing the same feeling.

Pulling down another picture showing a primitive airplane and two men standing by it, the teacher said, "These are the famous Wright Brothers who reached their dream because of their tenacity."

She laughed from sheer amusement as if savoring a silent joke. "Forgive me for laughing, but as the story unfolds you will see they had their humorous moments."

She began teaching as the five took notes.

"The Wright Brothers, Orville, 32, and Wilbur, 36, were not engineers; they were high school drop-outs who owned a bicycle shop in Dayton, Ohio. In 1899, they began their methodical survey of existing aviation literature—little more than a confusing collection of rumors and untested theories. Over the next four years they developed and tested their own theories.

"Inspired by German engineer Otto Lilienthal's success in glider flying, Wilbur Wright concluded that the secret to flight lay in developing air-worthy rigid wings. The brothers conducted thousands of experiments of each part of the airplane, including testing scale models of over 200 wing formations in a wind tunnel they built themselves.

"After signing contracts in 1908 with both the United States Army and a French commercial concern, the Wright Brothers gave public demonstrations of their airplane and astounded a skeptical world. René Gasnier, a French aviator who witnessed one of Wilbur Wright's flights in France, exclaimed, 'Compared with the Wrights, we are as children.'[2]

"One of the five spectators at the Wright Brothers' first flight was John T. Daniels, a patrolman at the Kill Devil Hills Coast Guard Station. Daniels remembered watching the Wrights during their first visit to Kitty Hawk and recounted his impressions in an interview for the September 17, 1927, *Collier's:*

'We couldn't help thinkin' they were just a pair of poor nuts. We'd watch them from the windows of our station. They'd stand on the beach for hours at a time just looking at the gulls flying, soaring, dipping....They could imitate every movement of the wings of those gannets; we thoughts they were crazy.'[3]

"They did not worry about what people thought about them. They were following their dream. They never gave up until they could finally fly."

She continued speaking in her convincing way. "Too many people quit just short of the goal. The tragedy of the Samoa jetliner several years ago which crashed, killing 95 of 101 aboard, bears this out. A Pan-American World Airways 707 jetliner went down just 1,000 yards short of the runway during heavy rains and burst into flames. Many people get into experiences that become as heavy rains to them. Their vision becomes fogged, they lose sight of their goal, and they crash not too far from the runway to victory."

She then handed the five some materials to study, rolled up the pictures of Roosevelt and the Wright Brothers and looked the five right in the eye, saying, "Life is not easy. The sun will not always shine. You will feel like quitting, but quitters never know the joy of winning. No matter how gray your life gets, do not give up or lose sight of your dream."

Waving with one hand, and with the other hand operating her electric wheelchair, she rolled steadily out of the room.

As Jonathan watched her go, he thought, "Now how did she know I felt gray today?" The days since the crash just seemed to float together from one inspiration to another. Each day met a new need or answered another question.

The five looked at one another and shook their heads in amazement at her courage and then settled down to some serious reading. As Jonathan looked through some of the material that she had given them to study, something interesting caught his eye. It was an article entitled, "The Rubber Man." He scanned over the material then settled down to read.

The scene was a winter day in 1839 at the General Store in Woburn, Massachusetts. The conversation around the old pot-bellied stove centered around a certain man who was not present at the moment. The men puffed at their pipes while a tall man spoke. "It seems a shame that we have to watch and can do nothing while a good man ruins his life. Charles has sold nearly everything he owned, and for just one purpose. He wants to buy more rubber."4

Another man spoke up and said, "They already have pieces of rubber all over their house. They have rubber stuck to walls, to tables, and to doors. Their home always smells of melting rubber. It is unbearable."[5]

"I really think Charles has gone crazy," the third man said. As they continued to talk, the object of their conversation walked into the store, dressed in a rubber coat and rubber shoes. He went over to the stove and began to warm his hands. The men in the room watched him. They looked at his hands, which were blackened and rough.

Charles said with twinkling eye, "Hello to all of you! Why is everyone so quiet? I have good news for you."

He reached into his pocket and took out a wad of black gummy rubber and said, "Look what I have been working on." The men stared at the stove. They would not look at Charles.

"Don't you want to hear my news?" Charles asked.

"Not again, Charles," said the third man. "We are your best friends, but we are tired of hearing about your experiments. You'll never find a way to keep rubber from melting in the heat of summer and cracking in the cold of winter. Why don't you give up this foolishness?"

"Foolishness!" Charles shouted. "It's not foolishness!" His voice quivered a little. "This is what I have to do! Don't you understand? This is my life. It is all I live for!" His small, strong hands worked with the ball of rubber, stretching it, pressing it. "Do you see how this rubber stretches? Don't you see the miracle in this little piece of rubber? Don't any of you realize what great things can come of it?"

The men shook their heads. One of them said, "I don't believe anything will come of rubber. You must be crazy, Charles, to think the way you do. How many years have you worked with this smelly stuff?"

"Five," Charles said. "And I will work five years more, or ten, or twenty. I cannot give up."

"You will die before you find this great secret you are looking for," said the tall man loudly. He knocked his pipe sharply on the top of the hot stove. "That piece of rubber in your hand is nothing but worthless black gum, and it's about time you admitted it."

"No, no, you are wrong," said Charles, becoming more excited. "You are all wrong!" He waved his arms. "Rubber will be important. Perhaps this piece of rubber holds the answer."[7]

"Ha! We have heard that before," they laughed.

"But this is different. I have mixed sulfur with this piece. I believe this will be the right way."

As the men taunted Charles, he grew angry and everyone began to speak at once. He waved his arms wildly trying to be heard above everyone talking at once, and suddenly the piece of soft, black rubber flew out of his fingers. It sizzled as it struck the hot metal of the stove.

The men were all giving reasons why he should give it up, but Charles was not listening. With a quick motion of his hand he swept the piece of rubber from the stove. He began to pull and tug at it. His eyes seemed to stare at something faraway. One by one, the men stopped talking. They realized Charles was no longer listening to them. He was thinking only of the piece of rubber in his hands. He began to speak like a man talking to himself.

"It could have melted," he said. "India rubber melts in heat. It becomes gummy, and then it melts; but this piece touched the hot stove and it isn't gummy."

His eyes examined the piece of rubber while his fingers continued to pull and tug at it. "Here it is charred and black," he said, "but just next to that charred part is a smooth section. It feels as smooth as paper."[8]

The men gathered around while Charles continued to talk. "Nothing I've ever done before has given me rubber that felt like this."

Suddenly, Charles held the piece of rubber up high and shouted, "I've found the secret! Now I know the secret!" He looked at the men around him, his eyes burning. He began to dance around the store. "Don't you see? This is the secret. Dry heat will cure rubber. It's the most amazing thing I've ever seen. I always believed that if there was one thing that would ruin rubber, it was heat, but that's not true. This piece tells me that. By mixing India rubber with sulfur and treating it with dry heat, I will make usable rubber."[9]

Jonathan glanced up from his reading and thought, "This man, Charles Goodyear, did not care that people thought he was crazy. He knew he was right and just never gave up."

Speaking out loud he said, "You guys feeling what I'm feeling?" A lively conversation took place from that one question of his and it was one they would never forget.

•••

Later that night as Jonathan prepared for bed, he sensed a change taking place inside of him. It was a good feeling, for too long there had been nothing but despondency that had dominated his thoughts. He smiled as he stretched his arms upward, thinking to himself. "Yes, my life is going to go forward again." Jonathan had trouble getting to sleep because of the excitement that welled inside him, which was a change. He used to have trouble getting to sleep because of boredom and restlessness. This was exhilarating.

As he looked into the darkness remembering all that was said that day, another thought flashed into his brain. He had once heard a man tell a story about a bulldog that sunk his teeth into a piece of meat and there was absolutely nothing that would make him let go of it. He determined in his heart to have the tenacity of that bulldog and never relinquish it when he entered back into the mainstream of life. This time would be different. Nothing would keep him down or stop him from attaining his dream.

Finding it hard to go to sleep, he flipped on the lamp by the side of the bed and wrote these words in the back of the notebook reserved for Reflections: "This day I choose to really live. I will choose to live enthusiastically! Action follows thought, so I will think power thoughts, filling my mind only with that which is good and inspirational. I will organize and live by a plan until I succeed."

5

TIME

*T*he banging on the door woke Jonathan who sleepily hollered, "Come in." Benjamin opened the door and brought a breakfast tray into the room and set it on the small table beside the bed.

He joked and said, "Looks like you overslept this morning, Jonathan. You weren't at breakfast so I brought it to you."

Sitting up and letting his feet touch the floor, Jonathan said, "This mountain air, good food, and relaxation is making me sleep deeply."

Benjamin was almost out the door as he called back over his shoulder, "I'll be back in an hour."

Jonathan proceeded to eat and then got dressed for the day. He later followed Benjamin to where the day's lesson would be taught. Coming to a small building he saw there was a large clock on the front door.

Wondering about this, Jonathan entered, and his attention was arrested by words written on the board at the front of the room: LIFE'S ACCOMPLISHMENTS ARE DETERMINED BY HOW TIME IS SPENT!

Greeting the other four who were already there, he sat down. Looking around, he noticed that on every desk there was an open dictionary. Looking down he saw highlighted the word: *emit:* "To send forth, to give out, or transmit. To exude, as fire emits heat and smoke, boiling water emits steam, and the sun emits light."

As he sat there thinking about this word a very elderly man came into the room, greeted them, introduced himself and began to speak. He wasted no time. He spoke forcefully, "What you give the world is determined by your stewardship of time. You can only give that which you have taken the time to learn, become or put inside you. Some things can give out only what they were predetermined to do, such as water.

"Water is a substance that emits steam when boiled, icicles when frozen, and needful fluid when drank. God and man are the masters of water. The water does not boil itself, freeze itself, or hop into your mouth for you to drink. What is emitted from water is determined by the control of man or nature's elements. It is not its own boss.

"The Niagara Falls, midway in the Niagara River, plunges 500,000 tons of water a minute into a steep-walled gorge. Both the Canadians and Americans use the falls for a great source of electrical power. The falls did not just decide to become Niagara Falls; they were placed there by God. They emit grandeur, beauty, and usefulness not by choice, but by placement.

"The difference in water and you is that you are free to make choices. After a choice is made you determine whether to stick with the choice. When you were growing up as a child you were more like the water. You went to bed at a certain hour simply because you were made to; now the hour you retire is determined largely by you.

"What you give yourself to is what you will become. What do you want to be in life? What do you want to do? What dream is hidden within your heart? Whether you reach your goals, see your dream come to pass, or give something of value to your world is decided by what you do with your time.

"Some people have the notion that to accomplish great things one must be at a genius level. This is not so. The great pianist, Paderewski, proves this. After performing brilliantly, a young enthusiastic admirer gushed, 'You are a genius! I wish I could play like you.' Paderewski made the statement that all realizers of dreams can relate to: 'No, I'm not a genius, I just practice eight hours a day.' To become the concert pianist that he was, he had to give most of his day working toward his dream before it became a reality."

The elderly teacher paused before going on. He looked at the five and said with emphasis, "Time is a gift. What you do with it is up to you! Listen closely as I play you a record that is now faint with age, but you can hear Thomas Edison, the inventor of the light bulb, echo primarily the same message."

Jonathan was surprised as he listened to Edison speak. These were his words:

"My third-grade teacher told me I was addled and not very smart, but she did not realize that what she was teaching seemed boring. My mind was on more exciting things. As I grew older an idea exploded in my brain. It became larger and more explosive until it consumed my thoughts. I started working on this dream so much that it took sleep from me. At times I was living on three or four hours of sleep a night because of the excitement that welled within me. Every waking moment I gave myself to my dream."

The record signaled it was finished by the raspy sound of the needle and the instructor stopped the old-fashioned phonograph. He spoke these words slowly and emphatically: "The realization of your dream can never be shared with others if time is not utilized properly."

The five paused for a moment of silence while the teacher was reaching into a drawer that he had opened with a key. He found the items he was looking for and then handed them to John to pass out. They were official-looking papers with gold embossed letters across the front.

The instructor began to speak again. "I am giving you this chart to put in your notes. Benjamin Franklin authored these thirteen rules and lived by them. He was a very successful man with many accomplishments in life, and gave our country many inventions that still help us today. Before you put these in your notebook look at number six: Lose no time. As Franklin realized that usage of time was important, so should those who wish to succeed."

The Professor instructed the five to glance over the thirteen virtues:

1. TEMPERANCE
Eat not to Dullness. Drink not to Elevation.

2. SILENCE
Speak not but what may benefit others or yourself.
Avoid trifling Conversation.

3. ORDER
Let all Things have their Places.
Let each part of your Business have its Time.

4. RESOLUTION
Resolve to perform what you ought.
Perform without fail what you resolve.

5. FRUGALITY
Make no Expence but to do good to others or yourself
(i.e. waste nothing).

6. INDUSTRY
Lose no Time. Be always employ'd in something useful.
Cut off all unnecessary Actions.

7. SINCERITY
Use no hurtful Deceit. Think innocently and justly;
and if you speak, speak accordingly.

8. JUSTICE
Wrong none, by doing Injuries or
omitting the Benefits that are your Duty.

9. MODERATION
Avoid Extreams.
Forbear resenting Injuries so much as you think they deserve.

10. CLEANLINESS
Tolerate no Uncleanness in Body, Cloaths or Habitation.

11. TRANQUILLITY
Be not disturbed at Trifles,
or at Accidents common or avoidable.

12. CHASTITY
Rarely use Venery but for Health or Offspring;
Never to Dulness, Weakness, or the Injury of your own
or another's Peace or Reputation.

13. HUMILITY
Imitate Jesus and Socrates.[1]

The Professor continued talking: "Great men and women from the past consider Benjamin Franklin's rule number six of primary importance. It is essential if one is to accomplish anything worthwhile in life. Time can never be brought back, for once it is gone it vanishes forever. Mr. Franklin, who utilized his time wisely, also penned these words: 'Dost thou love life? Then do not squander time. For that is the stuff it is made of.'[2]

"Sir Isaac Newton is an example of this. Someone asked him, 'How did you discover the law of gravity?'

"His reply: 'By thinking about it all the time.'"

The teacher said it again, "What you give yourself to is what you become.

"Before I leave today, let me share one more thought with you. It is simply: Number your days. I will leave you to mull over what has been presented, and to do your study assignments." With those words, he pushed a button on the recorder and exited out the door.

These words filled the room. "Organize your days, number your days, organize your days, number your days." As the message repeated itself over and over, John jumped up and pushed the stop button on the machine.

"Drives a man crazy," he said.

The five agreed and had a lively discussion about the thirteen virtues written by Benjamin Franklin. After they had settled down, Jonathan thought, "I organize, plan and dream, but my schedules and plans seem to fall through. It looks good on paper but it never comes to fruition. Maybe in the next two weeks one of the teachers will discuss how to make them happen."

Although he was somewhat frustrated, he did acknowledge in his mind that the tarnished dream he had almost given up was beginning to shine again. Rising from his seat and walking to the door, he told the others he would see them at dinner. Keeping time with his thoughts, he walked slowly back to his humble quarters, where upon entering he stretched out on the bed. Looking out the window, he viewed the majestic mountains that surrounded the place. He then slept awhile and was awakened by the call to dinner. Quickly jumping up, he combed his hair, splashed water on his face and ran to the dining hall.

Looking around the room, he noticed everyone was seated around the President, Mr. Theodore. With a happy feeling, he joined them and was kidded about his need for a beauty rest.

While consuming piles of fish, cornbread, potatoes and vegetables, the five sat around the table listening to the President tell a story. He told them about another president. His words vibrated with emotion. "When Bishop Hughes was president of DePauw University, there came into Depauw one of the most awkward looking greenhorns that ever came to college. He had on a pea-green suit which he had outgrown and didn't know what to do with his hands.

"His mother and father sent him to college and wanted him to have a good education. They lived on what they used to call a slanting farm. He hadn't learned all the city ways, but it didn't take him long to learn what a hot iron and a damp cloth could do to his breeches. He learned how to dress and it wasn't long until the girls discovered him.

"He was chosen as the honored speaker on Commencement Day. Early Monday morning of Commencement Week, when the train stopped at the depot, two of the funniest folks you ever saw got off. The old man had an accordion suitcase, and the dear old lady had an old-fashioned dress, but this country boy did not care. They were his father and his mother.

"He picked the little lady up in his arms and he kissed both her cheeks, and he took them up and introduced them to Bishop Hughes and to all of his fraternity brothers and girl friends. They were his father and his mother. They had been the creators of his very life. They had given him his heart and spirit and inspiration, and he was not ashamed of them, no matter how they looked or the way they were dressed.

"And then came that great address on graduation day, and he held that audience spell-bound, and in the silence that fell over them when he was through, as the people were sort of taking a breath, a man sitting behind the strange old couple saw the boy's father lean over to the dear old lady and then heard him say: 'Well, Mother, I guess that is about the best crop we ever raised.'"[2]

When Mr. Theodore finished telling the story, the five were trying hard not to show emotion, but they all were touched by it. They were either remembering the parents they had back home, or some parents they never had, for there was one among them who was an orphan. Benjamin broke the spell by walking up to them with some Ping-Pong paddles and balls, suggesting they play some tournaments.

છ•ન્

Jonathan went to sleep that night thinking about that awkward boy from the slanting farm that had made good. Then as he was drifting off to sleep his mind was filled with inspiration as he thought of Benjamin Franklin and all his accomplishments.

The next morning after breakfast when Benjamin came to get him they walked some distance until Benjamin said, "Well, here we are. We call this room, 'The Thief of Dreams,' for the subject of this lesson today has stolen many dreams through the ages. Just go on in and your teacher will probably be there."

Jonathan waved at Benjamin and approached the closed door cautiously. Everything about this place was a little different. He was not sure what to expect next. He opened the door slowly, peered in and found that the room was empty. He walked in and sat down in the dead quiet room waiting for someone to show up.

6

THE THIEF

t was not long until Michael, John and Joe showed up, followed shortly by Tim. The five talked about what had been happening inside of them this week and the new inspiration that they were feeling. They looked at their watches after twenty minutes had passed and decided to go outside and look around. When they rose, there suddenly came a little man into the room. They all sat back down as he began to speak.

"The reason for me being late today was to teach you a lesson. I put off coming in here today as long as possible. What happened today is called *procrastination:* putting off what can be done now. This trait has destroyed many a dream. The feeling, 'I can always do it tomorrow' keeps the dreamer in a state of false security, thinking he will do it someday. It gives him self-satisfaction because he has not thrown his hands up and quit. He knows in the back of his mind that his dream will be there tomorrow when he is not so busy.

"Because of this habit of procrastination, the inspiration for a certain thing grows rusty. It sometimes loses its luster and the dream that once burned within, now is a misty, fog-shrouded idea. The dreamer is lulled into thinking he still has a dream by projecting it into his future plans.

"You think, 'Today there are too many things that have to be done. The lawn has to be mowed, plants have to be watered, the garbage dumped, necessities need to be bought, and the car needs to be fixed. There is the house that needs to be cleaned, meals to be prepared, the laundry beckons, and the boss is waiting.' The list becomes endless with all the things that living requires you to do.

"How does one squeeze in time to realize a dream when they are so busy surviving? Is it possible to work on a dream and take care of all the necessary things required for mere existence?

"Yes, it is possible! This attitude separates the fulfilled dreamers from the wishful thinkers. Somehow in the merry-go-round, jet-speed age, the dreamers make time to pursue their dreams.

"You learned yesterday one must number or organize his days in order to realize his dream. The fact is established that every dream must have a plan of action. When that plan is formulated, then the real work begins. It is hard work bringing a dream from its infancy into ripe fulfillment. This is where the majority of people settle for less.

"For example: If your dream includes being an accomplished musician, you cannot sit around playing little fun, easy tunes. There comes a time when you must sit for hours practicing over and over again an intricate fingering pattern. You must practice until you reach your goal for that day, not just when you tire of practicing. You must practice until you attain even if it causes frustration and pain. There is no easy way of being a master at the piano. Let us look back into time at a little boy who became a great composer and musician."

The teacher paused briefly as he pulled down a drawing of Beethoven, and then began speaking again.

"In 1770, hidden away on the third floor of a house on the Bonngasse in Bonn, Germany, in an attic-like room dimly lit by a dormer window, a birth cry marked the arrival of a tiny baby who would rise from poverty and obscurity to change a musical world.

"The little baby had a father whose thirst for wine kept his family in poverty and who seemed oblivious to the suffering of his impoverished wife and children. One thing the father had though, was a keen eye when it came to the natural talent one of his sons had. He thought it would provide the family with another needed breadwinner.

"He became so possessed with making his son a competent musician that he forced the boy of five years old to practice hour after hour even while tears streamed down his face. Little Ludwig Beethoven was scolded, punished, and forced to practice on the clavier and violin. He would much rather have run down to the banks of the Rhine to watch the river barges go by.

"One friend of Johann Beethoven, Ludwig's father, recalled that he and Johann would often come home late at night from the tavern, get the tiny fellow out of bed, and keep him playing at the clavier until morning. The thing that he was forced to give himself to was what he became.

"Today Beethoven is considered to be one of the greatest musicians that ever lived. He was forced to practice daily by a drunken father who was driven by need and greed. Little did the boy of his father realize where the daily application of practice would take him."

The elderly teacher paused as the story of Beethoven's early life spun in their brains. He then continued very forcefully with these words:

"Each of you must include in today's plans something that will propel you into tomorrow's dream. It is not easy, but it is a must. If you keep putting it off for a better time, the better time will never arrive, for there will be other complications."

His eyes bored into their eyes as he emphasized these words, "A dream is realized when daily application is applied. What you give yourself to is what you become. If you give yourself to idleness, you get nothing in return except for a sour taste in your mouth and dull ache in your heart. Those that give themselves to leisure and play end up non-achievers. The people you remember who did something for their generation are the ones that gave themselves to a cause."

Jonathan looked closely at the older man and it seemed as if his whole body vibrated with what he was now saying. He believed it! The teacher's voice took on new emotion as he said, "You become what you give yourself to daily. You cannot be like a butterfly flitting from one project to another never staying long enough at any one thing to finish it."

His eyes became dreamy as he said the next words: "If you want to become a chemist you must spend years of consistent study and hard work to realize your dream. It is a very rare thing for a dream to be realized by just rocking in the rocking chair on the front porch. Consistency, pain, grit, determination and frustration all accompany the dreamer on his road to success."

He became so excited about his subject that he began knocking on the podium as his voice rose in pitch saying, "Every day you wake up you will decide what you will become that day. At the end of a year you will have accumulated 8,760 hours of choices. Always remember, time is one of the greatest gifts you will ever receive."

Jonathan looked around at the other four and wondered if they were thinking what he was thinking: "Was time a gift? How many people looked at it that way. How many hours were squandered and wasted by each human being?" He thought, "This man talked as if time were the key to getting things done. Maybe there is truth in his words."

The teacher spoke again, "It was said that Abraham Lincoln taught his conscious mind and deliberate will to rule his spirit and direct his energies. He had powerful self-control. This is essential to realizing your dream. Self-restraint is power and power is refreshing and glorious."

The professor stopped as abruptly as he has started. He gave the five their afternoon assignments and reading material and left quickly out the back door. His words echoed around the room. Beethoven, determination, procrastination, grit, pain, self-control, time and choices.

After the teacher left, Michael spoke with much feeling. "That story of Beethoven brought back memories. I had a father like his father. No, my father was not a drunk, but he pushed me to play the trumpet. It was like an obsession with him. He seemed to want it more than me, but something has started stirring within me since I've been here that I can't shake. I'm getting the itch to play again. You know, I was pretty good and I can still feel the exhilaration of playing before the crowds and hearing their applause. I never thought of it before in the sense of being able to help mankind through music, but people need music to make their lives a little easier."

The five sat there, each with his own private thoughts, thinking of the things they could do and become, but had procrastinated in doing. After reading and studying awhile, one by one they said their good-days and left the classroom.

ॐ

That evening after dinner Jonathan went to his room, opened the small window, and stared into the shadows gathering in the mountains. His brain was stuffed with new inspiration and excitement. He felt like it would be a long night, but found out later that when his head hit the pillow sleep overtook him. His body was still recuperating from the crash.

As morning dawned he dressed quickly and made his way to the dining hall, joining the others for a delicious breakfast. Later when Benjamin came to the cottage to get him for the day's lesson he asked him the question that had been on his mind the day before.

"What did the elderly teacher of yesterday's lesson do for a living before he came here?"

Benjamin looked thoughtful for a moment and then said, "Strange isn't it? Almost invariably the students want to know more about him. He was a very successful chemist and was considered to be tops in his field."

"He was so on fire with what he was saying," Jonathan said, "that it made us want to go home and start doing something worthwhile."

"That is good," Benjamin responded with a smile. When they had walked a little further he said, "Well, here we are. Just go on inside and expand that brain of yours."

"If it expands much more, I am afraid it will pop," Jonathan said with a grin.

Waving good-bye to Benjamin, he felt a loss, for he was getting attached to the older man. Benjamin had a way about him that made others walk taller in his presence and that seemed to bring out the best in people.

7

UNQUENCHABLE DESIRE

As Jonathan walked into the room he was soon groping around trying to find his way, for no sooner had the door closed behind him that the room became total darkness. It was not long until he felt hands touching his and he said, "Who is it?" A voice said, "This is Joe." They both burst out laughing, for they were in total darkness trying to find a light switch. After finding the other three guys, they decided to leave because they could not stand the blackness. As soon as they found the door leading to the outside, a light flashed at the other end of the room.

The five paused and glanced around and saw that on the wall was a large picture of a man who appeared to be from the 1800's. They noticed a tall dignified man sitting down in the center of the room running the projector that had flashed the picture on the screen. The man turned and said, "Sit down, young men, and we will begin today's lesson."

Jonathan dropped into a seat near the back while his friends seated themselves nearby. "The reason for the darkness," began the man, "was to acquaint you with what much of our world would be like if a certain man had not had a fervent desire to fulfill his dream. The man you see on the screen is Thomas Edison. Let's watch him for a few minutes and see how he was consumed with a dream."

As the projector whirled, picture after picture portrayed a man obsessed by a dream. It seemed as if he ate it, slept it, and lived it. It was never far from him and it influenced his very existence. Everything revolved around his dream. There he was working into the night while the rest of the world slept. When everyone else was canoeing, picnicking, shopping, or lazing around on Saturday, he was at work in his laboratory. It was not a job to him. His eyes shone with the excitement of his dream. It seemed that his very being was on fire with the passion of seeing his dream come into reality. The five listened as the film gave some of the high points of Edison's life.

He was born in 1847 and spent his childhood in poverty. He attended school for only three months before his teacher told him to drop out because he was hopelessly stupid. The intelligent teacher is unknown, but everyone knows Edison.

Edison's hearing had been impaired by a bout of scarlet fever. Deafness would trouble him for the rest of his life, but he did not let that kill his dream. Without a formal education, Edison educated himself while he worked on his inventions. He lost his job on the railroad because one of his experiments caused a train to be set on fire.

Soon afterward, he saved the life of a stationmaster's son, and the grateful father made Edison an apprentice telegraph operator which introduced him to his life's obsession: electricity.

Others had a dream of inventing an electric light. Seventy years earlier in England, Humphrey Davy had produced a glaring light by passing current through two sticks of charcoal, but after several minutes the charcoal was burned to cinders.

Throughout the 19th century, inventors had encountered the same problem. Electricity quickly melted the filament (the substance the electrical current passed through to produce light). That is why others failed. Their lights would only burn a few minutes.

For one year Edison worked twenty hours a day with his five assistants. After trying many different experiments he manufactured carbonized cotton thread and used it as a filament. He also enclosed it inside a glass bulb—creating a vacuum inside—removing the oxygen which caused the filament to burn.

On October 21, 1879, Edison invented a light that burned for over forty hours which quit only because he increased the voltage to see how much the filament would take before burning out. He realized his dream at 32 years of age.

When the film finished, the tall dignified man began to talk. "As you can see from the film, your dream has got to be in your subconscious mind, always there. It is not something you take out on Sundays, but it is your constant companion. It must whisper to you, nudge you when you're asleep, compel you when mediocrity calls. Anyone who realizes his dream will walk this kind of life. You must never give up on your dream because of people's opinions."

"An example of that kind of person was C.T. Studd.

"He was famous as one of the best cricketers in England at the time his father was the Lord Mayor of London. In his bedroom he and his brother practiced every detail of batting and bowling for hours at a time, day and night.

"C.T. never did things halfheartedly, including when he made a decision to go to China as a missionary. 'All in all or not at all,' summed up his philosophy. One example of his thoroughness was the fact that he insisted upon mastering the Chinese language and adopting the native dress and food. Because of his dedication he became one of the greatest missionaries to China just as he had been one of the greatest cricketers of his day. Whatever he did, it literally controlled his life with a deep burning passion."

The intense man paused and looked the boys in the eye before saying, "As Edison and Studd, you must embrace your dream or purpose; be on fire with it, and toil long hours to realize it." The older man then gave the five some reading material and notebooks to work on, just as the other teachers had done, bid them good-day and left the classroom.

As Jonathan sat there in the quietness, he could not seem to shake the intensity that the teacher and the two men he talked about portrayed. It seemed as if their influence permeated the room, trying as if it were to stir the fires of desire to a brighter glow.

One by one the five left after working for several hours. Each closed the door behind him, but none left the lesson there. With each step there was a crunching sound on the forest floor as well as an echo in Jonathan's ears, "Unquenchable desire, burning desire, fervent desire, intense desire." It stayed with him the rest of the day and into the night, ringing in his brain even as he fell asleep.

8

THE SPOILER

Morning ushered in a bright sun which streamed through the window straight into Jonathan's eyes, causing him to awake with a start. He dressed excitedly, ran to the dining hall, and greeted everyone with a big hello. He felt this was going to be a good day. After leaving the dining hall, he walked back to the cottage that had become his temporary home and got all his notes together before Benjamin came to take him to the lesson site.

Then going outside he waited on the porch for Benjamin. Seeing him approaching he walked towards him. They then walked side by side, enjoying the cool mountain air, to a building set apart from the others. Jonathan opened the door and all around the room there were shadowy pictures hanging on the wall. The instructor did not greet the five with a normal "Good morning." Instead he was saying, "O, consistency, thou art a rare jewel." He repeated it several times and Jonathan thought, "He sure is a strange man." Finding a chair near his friends, he nodded to them and sat down. When he was seated, the instructor then focused his attention on them and smiled a distant smile as if thinking of other things.

He began his lecture again with the words that he had just stated, "O, consistency, thou art a rare jewel." He then stopped and pointed to the shadowy pictures and said, "These are men and women that could have been remembered for a great work, but they are foggy shadows. We do not know who they are. Why? Because they did not learn to be consistent. They started great things, but they never finished them.

"They were attacked, as if by a serpent when he is least expected to strike. The spoiler, *inconsistency*, steals your dream from you subtly. No bands are played, no announcements are declared; one day you wake up empty because of this one thing. It is a poison that lurks in the mind and says, 'Do it today, but let up tomorrow, you can always do it next week.' Somehow that tomorrow never comes to many people.

"If you worked every day on reaching your dream, you would definitely be in the small percentage of people that accomplish what they set out to do in life. Let us look at a man who did just that. There have been thousands of clergymen, but very few have affected their world such as John Wesley. Why?

"Every day he rose at 4:00 a.m. Nothing was allowed to disturb his schedule. His love of orderliness and a good index of the mind was seen not only in the neatness of his dress, but in every area of his life. He prayed, studied, and meditated sometimes up to eight hours a day. He averaged fifteen sermons a week. He became the most devoted and successful evangelist the Christian Church has known since the early Apostolic days. He was beyond seventy years old when 30,000 people gathered in Cornwall to hear him speak. He drew a crowd even in his later years and became what he gave himself to consistently."

The professor paused for a few moments and then continued: "Procrastination and inconsistency are similar but different. Procrastination always puts things off. The mind says there will always be a better day. Things will become more conducive to succeeding. However, inconsistency burns up the fuel of inspiration, works fervently for a spell, and then lapses back into a do-nothing state for too long of a period. It becomes an eternity instead of a rest.

"Longfellow said:

The heights by great men reached and kept,
Were not attained by sudden flight;
But they, while their companions slept
Were toiling upward in the night.

"It is best described by a simple story loved by children around the world: *The Hare and the Tortoise.* The hare burned the rubber running fervently until he looked back and saw the tortoise plodding along. The hare decided to take a short rest and fell asleep. While he slept, the tortoise consistently plodded along and won the race.

"Quiet, consistent efforts are better than storms of flurry, punctuated by long winter naps. Times of inspiration are wonderful and needful, but do not stop just because you enter a period of plodding. Consistent, regular, constant duty and an unwavering purpose will let the world hear the music hidden within you."

The teacher paused and walked to the side of the room where there was a plaque inscribed with large letters some words penned by Elbert Hubbard. He then asked Tim to read it aloud and Tim read masterfully:

Genius is only the power of making continuous efforts. The line between failure and success is so fine that we scarcely know when we pass it; so fine that we are often on the line and do not know it. How many a man has thrown up his hands at a time when a little more effort, a little more patience, would have achieved success. As the tide goes clear out, so it comes in. In business, sometimes prospects may seem darkest when really they are on the turn. A little more persistence, a little more consistency, and what seemed hopeless failure may turn to glorious success. There is no failure except in no longer trying. There is no defeat except from within, no really insurmountable barrier save our own inherent weakness of purpose.[1]

As Tim finished reading, silence filled the room as the words seeped into their brains. The teacher was also silent as the words spun around the room. He then began to speak, "Long-fellow also said, 'The lowest ebb is the turn of the tide.' Do not give up in your purpose or work, but consistently keep at it, and the tide will someday turn. Your dream will come to pass."

He then walked to the corner of the room where there stood a large tree and as he pointed to it he began to speak. "The early Greek philosopher Epictetus said, 'No great thing is created suddenly, any more than a bunch of grapes or a fig. If you tell me that you desire a fig, I answer you that there must be time. Let it first blossom, then bear fruit, then ripen.'[2]

A consistent growth is essential for the bearing of fruit. If growth stops, the tree dies. A tree is a consistent thing. As soon as it takes root it is constantly doing something about growing and becoming a greater tree. In the winter, though it be covered with snow, it is preparing for springtime. The bursting of the green buds shows the consistency of the winter root-feeding. It is an ever ongoing, consistent cycle.

"Alexander Hamilton, the first Secretary of the Treasury, who was killed by Aaron Burr, penned these words before his death:

> Men give me credit for some genius. All the genius I have lies in this: When I have a subject in hand, I study it profoundly. Day and night it is before me. My mind becomes pervaded with it. Then the effort which I have made is what people are pleased to call the fruit of genius. It is the fruit of labor and thought.[3]

"Consistent labor, thought, and plodding through tons of information brought him to the label of genius."

The teacher then walked back to the center of the room, and pulled down a chart containing the picture of George Washington Carver.

"Birth does not dictate what you become. *You become what you give yourself to consistently.* George Washington Carver was born to slave parents near Diamond Grove, Missouri, in 1859. He determined he was going to be more than a slave. He became interested in rocks and plants and that interest took him to Iowa State College from where he graduated in 1894 and became a part of the faculty there. In 1896 he joined the staff of Tuskegee Alabama Institute at the invitation of Booker T. Washington.

"In 1916, Carver became a Fellow in the Royal Society of Arts in London, an honor given to few Americans. He won the Spirgarn medal in 1923 for distinguished service in agricultural chemistry. He became collaborator in the Bureau of Chemistry and also in the Bureau of Plant Industry of the United States Department of Agriculture in 1935. He received the Roosevelt medal in 1939 for his many valuable contributions to science. By the time of his death some eighteen schools had been named in his honor.

"It was said of him that he worked many long hard hours in his laboratory on a consistent basis to give the world what he gave them. What were some of his 'gifts'? Carver made more than 300 products from the peanut. They ranged from instant coffee to soap and ink. He made 118 products from the sweet potato, including flour, shoe blacking, and candy. He produced 75 products from the pecan. He made synthetic marble from wood shavings, dyes from clay, and starch, gum, and wallboard from cotton stalks.

"He could have whiled away his time by the enticing river banks and other places of interest, but he determined to become a person of value. He was consistent in his endeavors and they paid great dividends.

"He became more than a slave. He reached up and touched the stars. His mind expanded into a gigantic ocean of thought and exploration. He did not let his circumstances keep him down. He cast aside the negative situation and zeroed in on the positive. He did it under great odds, and that makes it even greater."

As the teacher finished his lesson he reached into the bottom drawer of his desk and brought out five packets of special reading and workbook assignments which he handed to the five. He then left the room with a wave of his hand. As they sat there it seemed that all the poetry and great words that had been spoken by men who had passed on were bouncing around the room.

Suddenly Tim spoke up. "I don't know if I can do all these things we're learning here. It sounds good and I know all the people the teachers are holding up for examples did it, but they did not live in this generation. It just seems like too much to expect. All the kids back home are on drugs, the families are all messed up, and the ghettos are black hell-holes." He finished with a sob of despair in his voice, while the others sympathized with him wondering what to say.

John spoke slowly as if weighing each word, "Tim, many great works of art and music were given to us by people that went through heartaches, brokenness, and had almost lost hope. The difference in those that make it and those that do not is simply the determination to keep pressing on even when things are pressing down on you. If you quit, you lose it all, but if you keep hanging in there, sooner or later something good is going to happen."

"I guess you're right," sighed Tim, "but sometimes it's so hard."

"Yes, life isn't easy," agreed John, "but it sure is a lot easier when you're up on your feet running towards a goal than just lying in the gutter."

As Michael, Joe, and Jonathan listened to the interchange between John and Tim, there was an unspoken determination within them that when they left this School for Dreamers they would work towards their goal instead of sitting down and quitting. It was a strong feeling.

They then settled down for some serious study and much later Jonathan left the room of the shadowy pictures and determined that he would never become a shadow like them.

As he crossed the pine-covered grounds with moss-covered tree trunks in bountiful array he could not help but think that something great and wonderful was happening to him. His thoughts were soon brought down to earth as he entered the dining hall and smelled the aroma of a delicious turkey. While he ate, the sun was slowly fading behind the trees, bringing a stillness and darkness only found in the mountains.

❧∞❦

That night after taking an extra warm bath and getting into his comfortable pajamas, he slid into the bed with delight. "Better enjoy while you can," he thought, "because soon the harsh realities of life are going to be upon you."

He went to sleep with the phrase, "O, consistency, thou art a rare jewel," going over and over in his brain. He determined to purchase that jewel and add it to his collection.

9

DOOM OR BOON

*T*he day dawned bright and beautiful, but chilly. Since it was early Jonathan decided to build a fire in the small fireplace. Everything needed—wood, paper and matches—was there. After getting the fire started, he sat in the old-fashioned rocker and listened to the crackling of the fire. The dancing flames became beacons to greater things as he thought upon his dreams, and all the things he wanted to do when he got home. He thought, "It doesn't matter if people know my name, but it does matter that the dreams inside of me come to pass. An idea brought into fruition and the fulfillment of a dream brings satisfaction and a glow of accomplishment."

As the fire burned down and the coals glowed in the fireplace he heard the call for breakfast. Hurriedly he jumped up and threw his clothes on, dashed out the door and down to the dining hall. There in the middle of the room another fire blazing in the fireplace eased the morning chill.

After eating a breakfast fit for a king, Jonathan left the room. As he was leaving he met Benjamin who was cheerful as always and told him he would meet him at his cottage in about thirty minutes. As Jonathan walked back to his cottage he mused over Benjamin's congenial, happy, and confident spirit.

As he neared the door he thought, "I better not dawdle because Benjamin is always on time and if I don't hurry I will be late." Sure enough, he was barely ready when Benjamin came for him.

They walked towards a building painted black. It looked dreary, drab, and not very inspirational. Jonathan did not want to offend Benjamin, but he could not keep the words from escaping from his mouth. "You expect me to have a lesson in that depressing place?" he exclaimed.

Benjamin said, "You might as well get used to it here, because life is full of highs and lows. You will have bleak days of discouragement, distress, and disillusionment, but you can control what they will do to you."

With those words he waved good-bye and Jonathan turned the knob and went in. It was no better on the inside, totally uninspiring; even the air was stale. He looked around and saw the other four guys looking about as excited as he felt. The man that came into the room was dressed in black and did not smile. The others were sitting there patiently, but Jonathan started to get up and leave when the teacher's voice stopped him in his tracks.

"Yes, go ahead and leave. That's what most people do when things go wrong, when it's gloomy and there's no song. They want to run, but if you are going to be successful in your endeavors, you must learn to go through the prisons of life, always reaching for something greater, never losing sight of your dream."

He paused and switched on a light which shone on a picture of a man sitting in prison.

"This could be St. Paul, John Bunyan, or many great men," he intoned, "but it is a man named Joseph."

He then turned on a recording that sounded like rats running, water dripping, cursing, angry shouting, and anything but positive. They listened as the narrator began.

"The man you see on the screen was put in that atmosphere by jealously, greed, and lies. He started off with dreams, but those around him squelched his ambition temporarily. He was sold by his brethren and taken into a foreign land where he found favor with an officer. It was in the officer's household that he was lied about again, which caused him to be placed in a damp dismal prison.

"Even though he was in prison he still had a dream. They physically abused him, stomped his integrity into the earth, humiliated him and gave him up for dead, but they could not kill his dream. It lived in the filth, muck, and mire of circumstances. It shone bright in the corners of his heart and mind.

"One day circumstances changed for him. He was remembered by a servant of the king. The king was in a dilemma and nobody could help him, but the servant remembered Joseph. He had given him answers while in prison, so why couldn't he help the king?

"His thought turned to action. He went straight to the king and informed him of Joseph's ability to interpret dreams. When the troubled king heard the exciting news, he immediately sent for Joseph. Of course, Joseph was able to interpret the strange dreams and because of this was elevated in the kingdom to a position second only to the king.

"The dream that he interpreted called for a man to be made ruler over all the land and store up food, for seven years of famine were coming. All the things that Joseph had said would take place, happened exactly as he had foretold.

"What a long, hard road he traveled to realize his dream, but it finally came to pass. The strange thing was that it was essential for the hard things to happen in order for the good to come out of it.

"Things that happen to you can be doom or boon. It is all in how you look at them. The finer things of life are usually connected with a tear or a crushing."

The teacher turned off the light switch and pulled down a screen with another picture on it. The five recognized it as being Abraham Lincoln. The teacher began to speak again. "It was said of Lincoln that he learned by his defeats. After he suffered humiliation at the hands of Stanton in the famous Reaper case, he returned from Cincinnati to Illinois to study law. He had learned something from a cruel disappointment, and he did not fail to make use of what he had learned. He disciplined himself through his disappointments.

"He did not succeed at everything he tried. In fact, he did a lot of failing; but did that keep him down? No! Ultimately he became President of the United States of America. His doom became a boon situation because he had a dream and a right attitude. His sincerity, rugged honesty, kindness of heart, and sense of honor paved a way to his fulfilling his ambitions."

He then pulled down a chart that looked interesting. With his black stick pointing at each fact, he began to read,

"Failed in business	*1831*
Defeated in Legislature	*1832*
Failed in business again	*1833*
Elected to Legislature	*1834*
Sweetheart died	*1835*
Suffered nervous breakdown	*1836*
Defeated for Speaker	*1838*
Defeated for Elector	*1840*
Defeated for Congress	*1843*
Elected to Congress	*1846*
Defeated for Congress	*1848*
Defeated for Senate	*1855*
Defeated for Vice President	*1856*
Defeated for Senate	*1858*
Elected President of U.S.	*1860*

And the name beneath this record of misfortune, crowned by final success? Abraham Lincoln." [1]

The teacher started to speak again in his dreary voice. He sure was not making this lesson easy for them, but it seemed to be part of the setting for this lesson—making nothing conducive to success.

He said, "Abraham Lincoln held power in reserve. He created it and conserved it, and on occasion he used it; he never wasted it in futile rage or unreasonable vexation over minor discomforts or in the weakness of self-indulgence.

"He had such self-control that he never touched alcohol or tobacco. He believed in temperance so much that when Reverend James Smith preached a sermon in which he called on the Legislature then in session to enact a law forbidding the manufacture and sale of alcoholic liquor for use as a beverage, a

71

strikingly advanced position at that time, Lincoln was one of those who, signing themselves Friends of Temperance, asked for the printing of the sermon.

"Lincoln said, 'The world's work must be done by men of initiative, passion, and power. It requires also men who do not waste the energy which their power produces, or enfeeble themselves in sensual self-indulgence.'"

The teacher stopped talking and all was quiet. He then told them that the subject of Abraham Lincoln would be discussed in another lesson. Pointing to a picture of a large man, he said, "John Bunyan was his name. He was born near Bedford, England, in 1628. Like his father, he became a tinker, or maker and mender of utensils. He received little education and served as a soldier from 1644-1646. He was married in 1648 to a religious woman and she influenced John to think seriously about God and religious things.

"He joined a non-conformist church in Bedford and soon began to preach there. He was arrested and put in jail for preaching without a license, and spent most of the next twelve years in prison. He was released in 1672, became pastor of his church and was returned to jail in 1675. That is when he began to write his famous book, *Pilgrim's Progress*. There probably never would have been this book if there had not have been a prison experience. He turned his doom into a boon situation.

"He did not let hate, bitterness and self-pity become his soul-mate in adverse circumstances; he turned a ruined life into a prosperous one."

The teacher then instructed them to look at a picture of a man on the back wall and proceeded to talk about him.

"That man had a great disappointment in his youth. He wanted to go to Yale more than anything, but his father told him that because his family was large, they could not afford to send him.

"Young William Cullen Bryant went to the woods to hide his disappointment from his father. He shuffled along the pathway as he thought about his future. He might have to give up the idea of becoming a writer; that in itself was a weight upon his shoulders. As he sat under the trees he heard a bird burst into song.

"That song gave him new hope. He decided to start making a living to help the family finances and on the side he would write the things in his heart. With this purpose he started back to his house and by the time he reached it all the bitterness and disappointment were forgotten. His mind was filled with ideas, words and singing phrases. He went at once to his room and began writing *Thanatopsis*. This became one of the world's most famous poems.

"He did not realize what a masterpiece he had written. He wrote it and put it in the top drawer of his desk with several other poems and things he had written. It remained unnoticed for six years.

"One day Bryant's father came across the poem and began reading it. He became very excited for he realized it was better than anything else the boy had written. He took it to one of the editors of the *North American Review*, who confirmed his opinion. When the poem was published in 1817 it created an immediate sensation. He turned his doom into a blessing.

"It does not matter what prison of disappointment you walk through, you can turn things around if you try hard enough and maintain an attitude of hope."

With those words, the teacher started putting things away, handed them their work and reading assignments and with a brisk wave of his hand was gone.

The five sat in the dark, black, gloomy room and pondered the things they had heard. Joseph's imprisonment, John Bunyan's imprisonment, Abraham Lincoln's failures, Bryant's disappointments, and then their own self-prisons came to mind. All off a sudden the lights went out and it was pitch black. They sat there for a moment trying to get their bearings, but could not see a thing. Then Jonathan remembered the room was totally in darkness because the windows had been painted black.

As he started to get up, he heard someone at the door. Glancing toward the noise, he saw the door opening and Benjamin standing there with a flashlight in his hand shining it into the room.

"Guys, we've had a power failure. Come with me to the dining hall and you can study by the kerosene lanterns and fireplace," he said.

As one voice they sighed with relief and gladly groped their way toward the door, relieved to get out of the blinding darkness. When they reached the dining hall, it looked cheerful and inviting. There seemed to be a festive atmosphere with the lanterns on all the tables and the fire blazing in the middle of the room. The day proved to be the best one yet, because they were not only studying, but talking and getting to know each other much better. Even the teachers were coming in and talking to them about things of interest.

They were surprised when dinner was announced. Time seemed to have flown. They put their books aside and sat down to a hearty meal of Hungarian goulash fixed with tender veal, dug into it and washed it down with apple juice. As soon as they finished their goulash and salad, the cook brought out hot apple pie that disappeared as quickly as it appeared. The five agreed that it was a satisfying ending to a different sort of day.

❧

Back at the cottage Jonathan decided to read a little bit by the kerosene lamp, so went he over to the available books and picked out a book of poetry by Bryant. Sure enough, there it was. *Thanatopsis*, a poem about death. "Just think of it," he thought, "this masterpiece was written by a teenager. It really does not matter how old or how young you are, it depends upon what you do with the circumstances life brings to you."

Suddenly the lights came on and he put out the lantern, got ready for bed and lay down. He thought, "Isn't it strange. When the light came on in my head, the light came on in the room."

Before turning out the lights for the night, he turned to the back of the notebook and again wrote in the section entitled "Reflections":

I determine to live life to the fullest. The poison of hate, self-pity and bitterness will be extracted from me by the power of love and determination. This day I will win and overcome every obstacle.

Later as he was drifting off to sleep, he determined that nothing was going to keep him from fulfilling his dream. He made up his mind that if prisons of discouragement, roads of adversity, and trials of despair were his lot, they would not stop him. His dream would grow and become, in spite of hardship, and doom would become a boon; difficulties would spur him on instead of burying him. He concluded that nothing was impossible if he believed and worked at it!

10

E PLURIBUS UNUM

*A*wakened by a dazzling sun, Jonathan's thoughts were of Abraham Lincoln and Joseph. Those men made it to the top in spite of unusual adversities and problems. They had exceptional character and were different from the norm. He roused himself from his reverie to open the door for Benjamin who had knocked. Benjamin had a brown paper bag tucked under his arm.

"Today your lesson will not be in the classroom," he said. "As soon as you eat your breakfast, put these hiking shoes on. You're going to need them where we are going. I will be back in a little while and we will have a thirty-minute hike to our destination."

It seemed only a few minutes had passed when the familiar tap came at the door. Jonathan hurriedly finished tying his hiking shoes, calling for Benjamin to come in. When Benjamin came through the door he handed Jonathan a light jacket and said he thought he might need it where they were going. As they stepped out into the crisp morning, Jonathan was thankful for the jacket and put it on, glad that it fit so well.

Excitement welled up within him as they joined Michael, Tim, John and Joe. He could tell they were just as excited. "Where are we going today?" Joe asked the question for all of them.

Benjamin just smiled and said, "Follow me."

The five followed Benjamin whom they could see was a real mountaineer. He had been over this ground many times before. The thing that amazed Jonathan about him was the fact that he seemed to be so in love with what he was doing. His spirit was contagious. He made others want to learn and achieve the same zest for life that he manifested. Jonathan mentally filed away in his brain to ask him later what it was that kept him so excited about what he was doing.

They were now climbing almost straight upward, and overhead was an exciting sight: a most beautiful eagle flying in the sky. It was breathtaking. They stopped in their tracks, staring at this majestic creature. Benjamin motioned for them to come up to a small spot at the top of the mountain.

It appeared to be a hollowed-out place, but one that was slightly camouflaged so that one could look out but not be easily detected. The five moved to where Benjamin had already settled in and waited for him to leave, wondering where the new teacher was.

He threw them an exciting glance, noticing their questioning look, and said, "I am your teacher today."

Jonathan, who was beginning to like Benjamin a lot, welcomed this information and expressed it simply by saying, "Great news!" His approval made Benjamin smile even more.

As the five made themselves comfortable in the little moss-covered indention in the side of the mountain, Benjamin pointed to the eagle and said, "That is what our lesson is about today."

They thought, "How could an eagle help us reach our dreams?"

As Benjamin continued to point towards the now moving eagle, he said, "Eagles have large, strong beaks and powerful claws which they use to build their nests and procure food. The eagle is not lazy, and he will not settle for a shoddy nest. It is a massive nest up to eight feet wide and often just as high. It would take two large wagon loads of material to build a nest or an eyrie. It is believed that eagles mate for life and come back to the same nest year after year. This in itself speaks of stability.

"Their flight is very graceful and they soar beyond the clouds. They can fly at great speeds and straight up and down. The American golden eagle, which we are watching, makes pin-point landings from great heights. With its broad tail and enormous seven-foot wings braced, the bird can maneuver its body so accurately it can land without a runway. Its strong breast muscles supply braking power."

Benjamin continued to talk. "The Romans used a golden figure of an eagle to represent strength, skill, and bravery. They placed it on the tip of a spear and carried it as a standard at the head of a legion. In 1782, the United States, under the Congress of the Confederation, took as its emblem a bald eagle with outspread wings, a shield on its breast, an olive branch in one foot, and a sheaf of arrows in the other. The eagle on the United States coat of arms carries a scroll in its beak bearing the Latin words, *E Pluribus Unum,* meaning 'one out of many.'"

Benjamin leaned back against the mountain and was quiet while the five absorbed what he had just told them. The last words he said, "One out of many," were what affected Jonathan the most. He stared quietly at the bird who was gracefully coming back to land on the edge of the nest. His thoughts were on the words that Benjamin had used to describe the eagle. He was a bird of strength, skill, and bravery, and he was not lazy. Jonathan noticed something. *The eagle was always busy looking intently at something; it was very alert and aware.*

He said to Benjamin, "He doesn't miss a thing, does he?"

Benjamin smiled while speaking slowly, "I'm glad you observed that. He acts as if he were excited to be alive. He doesn't let life pass him by. He lives life to the brim. He is in control of his surroundings and will fight any other bird that threatens him. He doesn't feel sorry about a situation and sit back and take it; he never lets go or never gives up."

They were quiet a few more minutes when Michael spoke softly into the stillness of the high mountain area, "Before coming here I was being just the opposite of that eagle. I had lost my zest for life. I had been giving in to life's hard knocks, allowing lethargy to overtake me."

The other four nodded their heads in agreement acknowledging the same. As they sat there, exhilarated by the fresh mountain air watching what most people never see, they openly spoke of becoming more determined to be men of stronger strength and character. They made a pact that they would be *E Pluribus Unum, one out of many!* and seek to be honest, hardworking, brave, courageous, responsible and trustworthy.

Benjamin, leaning back against the mountain, started talking to them again. "You know there was another young man who had many odds against him. Abraham Lincoln was born and raised in poverty. When he was seven the family moved to a location across the Ohio River called Pigeon Creek, which is now Spencer County, Indiana. The first winter they did not have a cabin, merely a rude shelter of poles, brush, and leaves enclosed on three sides and called a half-faced camp. When Thomas Lincoln, his father, got around to building their cabin, it had at first neither floor, door, nor window. The family fare was a matter of game animals, honey, birds, nuts, and wild fruits.

"Abraham worked hard at helping to build cabins, splitting fence rails, planting corn and assisting in other rough tasks. He also found time to fetch books by walking many miles to attain them, and studied them in his spare time. He also showed a fondness for speech-making, mimicking the preachers and orators who penetrated to the rough creekside area. Additionally he was able to earn a few extra dollars by rowing passengers from the shore to passing steamers.

"Even as a lad he was never lazy and that trait followed him into young manhood. When he was 22 he managed a mill and conducted a store with W.F. Berry, who died leaving a heavy debt ($1,000.00), which Lincoln finally paid. He was busy at many things trying to earn a scant living. He acted as village postmaster, traversed the county as deputy surveyor, and all the while read law, studied grammar, and followed the trends of national politics.

"Once he made a mistake in the weighing of tea by using a lighter weight than he intended. He did not rest until he had carried the additional few ounces of tea to the woman to whom it belonged. He was that kind of young man—very conscientious. He was patriotic and noble and left behind him a creed that all young men could follow."

Benjamin stopped talking and pointed again to the eagle. "Did you see that? He dipped down to the earth, probably after a prey."

The five watched the eagle and then listened to Benjamin as he continued talking about Abraham Lincoln. "One writer wrote, 'America that produced Abraham Lincoln can beget other sons in his likeness and train them up in his spirit.'"

Benjamin looked at them and said, "I believe I am sitting with five young men that have the potential to become as Abraham Lincoln in spirit."

He then opened the lid of a small basket he had been carrying and the sight of food made their mouths water. As he spread a cloth on the uneven ground and removed the food from the basket, he said, "Remember you are what you eat *mentally* and *physically*. Just as you need to instill inspirational things into your mind, you need to eat the right food."

The foods he had brought looked delicious: lots of fruit, whole-wheat chicken salad sandwiches, juices and other things. They enjoyed a wholesome lunch, and helped Benjamin put the leftovers back into the basket. He then said they would be starting back to the camp.

They took one last look at the eagle who was once again soaring gracefully and skillfully high into the clouds, then started following Benjamin back a different way than they came.

As their feet made crunching sounds against the twigs and fallen pine needles, Jonathan could see and feel inspiration all around him. The majestic towering trees even seemed to point upward. He thought, "If I could just take this feeling with me."

Benjamin said, "Now you want to lock this feeling and these pictures inside your mind, so when you get into the crowded valley, you can escape to this place in your thoughts."

"Now, how did he know what I was thinking?" Jonathan thought. He started noticing details that before had escaped his attention. The squirrels jumping from tree to tree, the swaying of the strong trees, the intricate leaf patterns, the green moss everywhere, and the marvelous pine smells were being imprinted upon his mind. He was determined more than ever before to pursue his dream and the finer things of life. He purposed to not live any longer in despondency, despair, and disillusionment, but to let his spirit soar as the eagle.

The five saw the white buildings through the trees and welcomed the sight, as their legs were beginning to tire from the climb up and down the mountain. When they entered camp, Benjamin bid them good-day and told them he would see them at dinner.

Jonathan went inside the house and immediately took a hot shower and stretched out on the bed for a short nap. It seemed like he had just gone to sleep when the bell for dinner sounded and woke him. He jumped up, rubbed his eyes, and walked quickly to the dining hall. When he entered the dining hall the food smelled wonderful.

After greetings were made, they all fell silent while filling themselves full of fish and chicken. They then played a few games of Ping-Pong and sat around talking about what they were going to do when they got back home. Benjamin said goodnight to them, and was just leaving when they heard him make a loud exclamation. They jumped up and ran to the door where he was, followed the direction of his eyes, and saw two bear cubs walking through the camp. Benjamin warned everyone to be careful because mama bears were sometimes dangerous around their cubs. He shined his flashlight on the cubs and they started running away. That night they walked with each other to the cottages, making sure everyone was safe.

After getting ready for bed Jonathan opened the window a crack to let in the refreshingly crisp air. As he laid down, the sore muscles in his legs reminded him of the trek up the mountain. "I must get in shape when I get back home," he told himself. His last thoughts were of the soaring graceful eagle.

11

AND THEN SOME

The tap at the door woke Jonathan with a jolt. "Come in," he called.

Benjamin walked through the door holding a rolled-up scroll-like paper. He handed it to Jonathan and said, "This is Abraham Lincoln's creed I told you about yesterday. It will be discussed in one of your classes, but I wanted you to have it now."

Jonathan thanked him, glanced hurriedly at it, then walked over and put it into the notebook marked *The Dreamer's Treasure Chest* that they had given him when he first arrived.

After breakfast, while walking with Benjamin, Jonathan noticed a brilliant sunshine that seemed to bathe everything he looked at with light and energy. He was feeling on top of the world when he saluted and waved to Benjamin as they came to the classroom. When he walked in he saw his friends gathered around a picture of Christopher Columbus, and below the picture was a monument with these words inscribed on it:

In the city of Valladolid, the ancient capital of Spain, is a monument erected to commemorate the discoveries made by Christopher Columbus. The most noticeable feature of the monument is a lion, with his paw raised as if to erase part of the words which had formed Spain's national motto: *Ne Plus Ultra* ("Nothing Beyond").

For many hundreds of years the sailors who ventured forth into the great Atlantic Ocean believed they had reached the boundaries of the Earth. Europe, Asia, Africa lay behind them, and there was nothing before them (as far as they knew) but the limitless expanse of the Atlantic Ocean. To them the coast of Spain was "Land's End," with *Ne Plus Ultra*—nothing beyond. But when Christopher Columbus returned from his eventful voyage in 1492 and reported discoveries of a vast continent and many islands, the motto was changed from *Ne Plus Ultra* to *Plus Ultra* ("More Beyond")![1]

Michael was speaking now. "Think about it! The whole world was locked into that conception, nothing beyond. One man with a dream and a belief proved they were wrong."

"Yes, more beyond," said a voice behind them. They turned and looked into the clearest blue eyes ever seen. They were eyes that literally could see beyond the norm.

"My name is Tetra, and I will be your teacher today," he informed them. They shook hands and found seats next to the window so they could see and feel the sunshine.

"We are going to talk about the concept, 'And then Some,'" Tetra began. "Most people do the norm, but then you have those that push on and do what others only dream of doing. They go beyond what is expected."

He pulled down a picture of a man named Ignace Jan Paderewski. "You may have heard of Paderewski while you have been here. His mother died soon after his birth and his father was sent to prison when Paderewski was only three years old. He was born in Poland at a time when the political condition was very revolutionary. The serfs were practically slaves. The Polish nobility, which owned the great estates on which these peasants lived, applied to the Russian government repeatedly asking them to free them, but the government always refused. It was not until 1861 that they, by the order of the Emperor, were made free everywhere.

"After his father returned home from prison they had to move to a new neighborhood. There his father was responsible for a new post in Sadylkow, a township of only 2,000 in population—1800 of them Jews. Paderewski could hear their wailing and crying at the cemetery not far from his house, so much that he seemed to hear it when he was older. He was a very lonely little boy and had no playmates.

"As a small child he loved the piano and nature. He was either climbing trees or at the piano. His teachers did nothing to help him learn, for they really did not know the piano well themselves. So he did a great deal of improvising since he had no access to musical compositions.

"At age 12 he gave his first concert and attracted the attention of a very wealthy family who took him to Kieff for a few weeks. He had never heard a singer, orchestra, pianist, or a concert. About this time, he was sent to a conservatory so he could have a real musical education. What a disappointment awaited him. His first teacher was so discouraging and unpleasant that he asked to be relieved from piano study. The teacher told him he did not have the hands for piano playing.

"Of course, he had a second teacher, but this teacher did not pay attention to necessary details, so he made little progress. At 16 years of age he finally was given lessons with the best piano teacher at the conservatory who told him, 'Now, I'll give you some good advice—do not try to play the piano, because you will never be a pianist. Never!'

"During this time of disappointment, he turned to composition. One day, when he was 19 or 20, he sold about nine pieces to Mr. Hugo Bock, a publisher. Mr. Bock then invited him to a dinner party he had planned for that evening. Mr. Anton Rubinstein was to be the guest of honor. Paderewski was so excited about this prospect he could hardly wait for dinner. After dinner Rubinstein asked him to play one of his newest pieces. After he had played, the great pianist said, 'You have a brilliant future. You have an inborn technique and you could have, I am sure, a splendid pianistic career.'[2]

"Later at age 24, the door was opened to him to study with the great teacher of that time, Leschetizky. The great teacher told him if he had only started earlier he could have become a great pianist. It was like he had been dancing without learning to walk. He had to start with basic finger exercises, because before this time he did not really know how to work or practice."

Tetra then put on a worn tape and had the five listen to some important things Paderewski had to say himself. They listened carefully as the older man's voice filled the room:

"There are a great many people in this world, who are struggling constantly, aspiring to some ideal, striving to satisfy their ambition, and who are handicapped in their striving, and constantly defeated in their efforts. I came to the conclusion, if one wishes that other people have pleasure from his playing, he must work. I did incessant work. The results of that time seemed rather meager to me. I was still seeking and longing for my heart's desire, but I had to learned how to work for it. Yes, I repeat to you, how to work, and this is of the utmost importance. I have said this before, but in the career of every artist, no matter what his profession, the knowledge of how to work is his greatest asset. I practiced eight or nine hours a day and was composing also, so you see I labored tremendously.

"Later at the beginning of my success, Leschetizky could not believe it. He could not understand how I could make good all those losses of my youth. He did not know that I was persistent, energetic, and physically enduring."

Tetra turned the tape off and then made a comment that spun in Jonathan's brain. "He became famous simply because he went beyond the normal procedure of piano practice. He did more than what was required of him."

Jonathan thought, "Nobody comes near making it without hard work and putting in more hours than are required. Columbus and Paderewski were driven by a dream and did not even count the hours. They were both faced with difficulties and impossibilities, but that did not stop them."

Jonathan determined that he would begin to work beyond and to adopt the "second mile" principle.

Tetra gave the five their work assignment and then bid them adieu. As they worked quietly, Jonathan heard in his mind the thunderous sound of the gigantic waves that were the constant companion of Columbus, and seemed to feel the rejection and unbelief that had surrounded Paderewski during a portion of his lifetime. He thought, "They could have been satisfied with less, but the gnawing inside of them would not let them. It was an inner belief that kept their faith high. They knew there were greater horizons; there was something beyond if they could just wade through the skepticism, reasoning, solid facts, and the 'you can't's.'"

After finishing their assignments one by one, each of the five walked out of the room with the sun shining brilliantly upon him.

They walked around the retreat area and noticed a little path that led into the woods. It looked inviting so they followed it a little way until they came to a sparkling clear stream. They took off their shoes and socks and waded into the water. On the other side of the stream was a bench made out of a huge log. Joe and Jonathan made their way over to it and sat down.

They rested on the bench talking for a long time while the others goofed off in the water. When the shadows of the forest started gathering they reluctantly waded back to the other side of the stream and just carried their shoes and socks back with them to their cottages.

Not long after Jonathan got inside he heard the call for dinner. After splashing water on his face and running a comb through his hair, he made his way to the dining hall once more. Meeting him at the door was Benjamin.

"It's been a great day," Jonathan told him. "One I'll never forget."

Them they all sat down to enjoy a delicious meal of barbecued chicken.

❧

Later that night as Jonathan finally was dozing off to sleep, he thought, "If Christopher Columbus hadn't gone beyond what everyone believed to be true, we wouldn't have been studying about him today. I wonder who else would have finally discovered the world was round instead of flat as originally believed? His dream and belief literally drove him on and then some."

He asked himself an honest question while staring in the darkness. "Would I have had the tenacity and grit to stick with something I believed in such as Columbus did?"

12

LEAVE YOUR STAMP

I t was a clap of thunder that jolted Jonathan awake. He looked at the clock and it showed the time to be 7:30 a.m. Looking outside he saw that it was dark and stormy. The sun was not shining and he just wanted to bury himself back under the covers.

He ran and closed the window that had been left open the night before and laid back down for another few minutes. While he laid there, he mused upon all that had taken place and knew that he would never be the same again.

Into his thinking processes also came the impression that something rather strange was taking place. He had the distinct feeling from time to time that somebody was following him. As he thought he remembered the previous day in the woods. He did not want to acknowledge it, but the feeling was there. Then he dismissed the thought, thinking that maybe he would find out before he left exactly what it was.

The tap that came every morning interrupted his thoughts. He glanced at the clock—it was 9:00. Hurriedly he jumped up

93

and pulled his pants on and opened the door. Benjamin walked in with a tray and said, "The electricity went off, so I brought your breakfast to you. It looks like a storm coming up today. When I come back later, I'll bring you a raincoat."

With that he left and Jonathan sat down to an appetizing breakfast which he thoroughly enjoyed. When Benjamin came back with a raincoat and hat, Jonathan followed him reluctantly out into the thundering storm.

They walked quite a distance before they reached their destination. As Benjamin hurried away, Jonathan went inside, stomping and wiping his feet on a rug, taking off and hanging up his hat and raincoat. He walked toward a seat near a heat duct and noticed that only Michael, John, and Joe were there. He asked them where Tim was and they told him he was not feeling well and that he stayed in bed.

Looking towards the front of the room they saw a beautiful older lady watching them with amusement. She inquired, "You don't enjoy the storm?"

"Not really," Jonathan said. "I like it if I'm warm inside, but not out in it. Of course, this room is nice and cozy, so it won't bother us."

She started to speak. "Well, today's lesson is about a man who caused a storm in the political arena of Britain, and became a whirlwind around the world. The name of the lesson is 'Leave Your Stamp.' We encourage you to make your mark. You can have other people influence you, but you must leave your stamp of originality on the world.

"If you think of some of the people that have left a mark on the world, you would find that each of them had their own distinction. They were not a carbon copy of someone else. Winston Churchill was known for his optimistic 'V' sign. Florence

Nightingale had her lamp. Woolworth conceived the idea of the five-and-ten-cent store. His fortune was measured by millions when he passed away. He took a different idea, and became successful all because he dared to leave his stamp.

"I am now going to show you a film about Winston Churchill." She walked over and punched two buttons at once. One turned the light off and the other brought a screen down low. She then switched on the projector and there on the screen loomed a man that changed history because he dared to stand up and leave his original mark. The film began with a great burst of music almost with the same intensity of the storm outside. They listened as the narrator began to talk:

"Winston Churchill was born to Lord Randolph Churchill in 1874. His father was too busy for him and did not understand his slow learning ability. Because of his backwardness in his studies he entered Harrow School, a leading English secondary school. He entered at age 12 and was lowest in the class until age 18.

"One of his instructors decided the only place for a boy of limited intelligence was soldiering. He entered the Royal Military College at Sandhurst. He had failed the entrance exams twice before passing them, but he soon led his class in tactics and fortification, the most important subjects.

"He graduated eighth in a class of 150 and in 1895 was appointed a second lieutenant in the 4th Hussans, a proud Cavalry regiment. In 1896 his regiment was sent to Bangalore in Southern India. There he acquired a fondness for polo and read many books he had neglected in school.

"In 1897 he took a leave of absence to become a reporter for the war between Northwestern India and the British forces.

After returning to Bangalore in 1888 he wrote about his experience in his first book, *The Story of the Malakand Field Force.*

"In 1898 he was transferred to the British force in Egypt that was going to invade the Sudan. He took part in the last great cavalry charge of the British army, in the Battle of Omdurman. He then returned to England and wrote a book about the Sudanese campaign, *The River War,* in 1899. At the same time, while working on the book, he ran for Parliament as a Conservative from Oldham. He lost his first election.

"The Boen war in South Africa began in October 1899, and a London newspaper hired Churchill to report the war between the Boers (Dutch settlers) and the British. Soon after Churchill arrived in South Africa, the Boers ambushed the train he was riding on, captured him, and put him in prison.

"Churchill made a daring escape. He scaled the prison wall one night and slipped by sentries. He then traveled by freight trains, crossing 300 miles of enemy territory to safety. He became a hero overnight.

"In 1900, he returned to England and to politics. Oldham gave him a hero's welcome, and the voters elected him to Parliament. In January 1901, Churchill took his seat in the House of Commons for the first time.

"In 1911, Prime Minister Herbert H. Asquith appointed him First Lord of the Admiralty. The vast build-up of German military and naval forces had convinced Asquith that the admiralty needed a strong man. Churchill was one of the few men in England who realized that war with Germany would probably come. He reorganized the navy, developed anti-submarine tactics, and modernized the fleet. He also created the navy's first air service. When Britain entered World War I, on August 4, 1914, the fleet was ready.

"In 1915, he met with a bitter disappointment when his attack on the Dardanelles and the Gallipoli Peninsula was not successful. He was blamed for it and because of this resigned from the admiralty, although he kept his seat in Parliament. He told one friend, 'I am finished.' He felt like a political failure.

"He was not really finished, but he felt like it. After World War I ended in November 1918, he became Secretary of State for War and for Air. In 1922, three days before the election he had to have his appendix removed, so did not get to campaign. He lost the election and said he found himself *without office, without a seat, without a party, and without an appendix.* '1

"In 1939, World War II had begun, the one Churchill had so clearly foreseen. He got his old post back. Prime Minister Neville Chamberlain named him First Lord of the Admiralty. The British fleet was notified with a simple message, 'Winston is back.'

"After all of this he became Prime Minister of Great Britain at the age of 66. He wrote later, 'I felt as I were walking with destiny, and that all my past life had been but a preparation for this hour and for this trial.' There had never been a national leader who took office in such a desperate hour. Churchill said to them when he was elected, 'I have nothing to offer but blood, toil, tears, and sweat.'

"On June 4, Churchill told Commons that even though all of Europe might fall, '...we shall not flag or fail. We shall go on to the end...we shall fight in the seas and oceans...we shall fight on the beaches, we shall fight on the landing-grounds, we shall fight in the fields and in the streets, we shall fight in the hills; we shall never surrender...' On June 22, France surrendered to Germany. Britain now stood alone.

Churchill declared: "Let us therefore brace ourselves to our duties, and so bear ourselves that, if the British Empire and its Commonwealth last for a thousand years, men will say, 'This was their finest hour.'"

"While the battle raged, Churchill was everywhere. He defied air-raid alarms and went into the streets as bombs fell. He toured RAF headquarters, inspected coastal defenses, and visited victims of the air raids. Everywhere he went he held up two fingers in a 'V for victory' salute.

"After the United States entered the war in December 1941, Churchill and President Franklin D. Roosevelt exchanged many messages. Churchill stirred all of America with his faith.

"In the midst of all his power and glory, in the year of 1945 he lost his post of Prime Minister and this defeat hurt him deeply.

"He was back again, though. In 1951, Churchill almost 77 years old, again became Prime Minister. One of his greatest honors came to him in 1953 when he was knighted by Queen Elizabeth. She made him a knight of the Order of the Garter, Britain's highest order of knighthood.

"In 1953, Sir Winston suffered a severe stroke that paralyzed his left side, but he made a remarkable recovery. Later that same year he won the Nobel prize for literature. He was honored for his mastery of historical and biographical presentation and for his brilliant oratory. He lived to be 90 years old."

The film was over. The lights went on and the five sat for a few minutes in reflection, musing over the powerful influence one man had on his world.

The teacher proceeded to talk again. "The film you just saw is a very moving account of what can happen when one person is not afraid to cast his own mold. When you think about the billions of people in the world and how not two of them have the same thumbprint, it is mind boggling. If we were all meant to be the same, there would not have been the need to make a separate print for each individual.

"There is another individual who left the traditional mold and made her mark simply because she did not feel comfortable being a social butterfly when there were so many hurting people all around her. Her name is Florence Nightingale."

The teacher then walked over to the side wall and pulled down a picture showing a woman of strength and then began speaking. "Florence Nightingale was born on May 12, 1820, to wealthy British parents. Her mother was very social and filled their house with guests. Florence had every opportunity to become a social butterfly. However, she did not want that to be her future. From a child she always enjoyed helping nurse sick babies and animals. When she turned 16 she made an important decision. She decided she must devote herself to service for others. Even though she made the decision, life continued on the same way. She and her sister were presented to Queen Victoria when they entered British society, and that was followed by travels to Europe.

"Florence had not forgotten her purpose in life. Slowly she began to realize what her work must be. 'She turned down suitors, declined many parties and spent much of her time studying health reforms for the poor and suffering.' 2

"Her family prevented her from working in a hospital for they thought hospitals were dirty and unfit for women. However, something happened to change her life. She went to study nursing at a hospital in Paris, and at age 33 became superintendent of a women's hospital in London.

"Later when Great Britain and France went to war with Russia in the Crimea in 1854, the Secretary of War asked her to take charge of the nursing. She sailed to Crimea with 38 nurses. This little band faced a job that seemed impossible. Five hundred wounded troops had just arrived from the Battle of Balaclava where the Charge of the Light Brigade had taken place.

"The hospital was an old Turkish barracks, huge, dirty and unfurnished. The wounded lay on floors, bleeding and uncared for...There were no cots, mattresses, or bandages. Miss Nightingale found a few men well enough to clean the place and put them to work at once.' 3

"She set up a nursing schedule for care, kitchen work and diets. She worked tirelessly. At night she walked with her burning lamp the four miles of corridors, and wrote countless letters demanding supplies of the British military officials.

"So successful was she that she was given charge of all the Army hospitals in Crimea. By the time the war was over she was a hero. She had saved countless lives and brought about a world-wide reformation in hospital administration and nursing work.

"She went beyond what was expected of her and changed history for the better. One woman who stepped out of the mold and stood courageous, believing in her dream, shook a 'world.'"

The teacher looked the five straight in the eye and said, "Now these two people we've studied about did not leave a mark because they wanted to be different. No, that was not their purpose. It went deeper than that. They had a dream or a cause that burned inside of them and even though the others around them did not share that same fire, it did not stop them from forging ahead in worlds unknown and fulfilling the dream that led them on. Just being different is not enough. That is not the point. The point is to bring your stamp upon your world— to follow the dream inside of you even if it is a new way. You have to do it although it may be original. Do not worry about being like somebody else, but give the world your flavor."

She then picked up a box and brought it over to each of their desks. She took out of the box a piece of paper and a small ink pad. She said, "Put your thumb on the ink pad and then press it on the paper."

They each did what she asked them to do and then she said, "Put that in your notebook as a reminder that the world is waiting for you to leave your stamp."

She then put the box up, gathered up her things, gave the five their daily work assignment, and smiled as she waved good-bye. Walking out the door, she looked back and said, "Oh, look! The rain has stopped."

Jonathan glanced out the window and found that the storm had passed over. He did not feel like doing the assignment quite yet, so just sat and soaked into his brain all that he had heard. Noticing that the others were working feverishly, he opened his notebook and started working and reading. The others finished before him and he was left alone.

After what seemed like a long while, he got up and walked out with new goals forming in his mind. He thought, "I could make a difference. To be world famous has nothing to do with it. That doesn't even matter. Realizing my dream is the important thing." The more he thought about it, the realization came to him that each person has a world to affect and even if they did not affect the whole world, they would affect their "world."

He decided to go for another walk in the quiet woods before returning to his cottage.

That night he took a shower and found a good book to read and settled down for an evening of relaxation.

He read for about three hours, then fell asleep, drifting off to a world of inspiration, history and challenge, seemingly dreaming all night. When he woke up the next morning, his brain was still whirling.

At about 10:00, walking with Benjamin to the classroom, he told him about his new inspiration. Benjamin just chuckled and said, "Today will bring you down to earth. It will be a lesson that will let you know that the glory of winning is not always found on a crowded way."

13

LONELINESS PRECEDES
THE GLOW

*J*onathan followed Benjamin to a building that was way out in the woods. He thought it seemed kind of lonely and forlorn.

As Benjamin left him there, he walked up to the door, pushed it open and walked inside. In the front of the room stood a white-haired lady that exuded strength and confidence. She seemed to have rivers of excitement and miles of smiles. Her spirit filled the room with sunshine.

He greeted his friends and noticed that Tim was back in class today. Then the teacher greeted them warmly and said, "When you all get settled, we will begin today's lesson."

The five found their places and got their notebooks out, ready to add another page of inspiration. The teacher then began to speak about struggling dreamers.

She said, "All dreamers have struggles and lonely days before they accomplish what they set out to do. Before you share the results of your dream with a world there will be many discouragements, disappointments and setbacks. Getting where you want to go is the difficult part. The applause of the crowd is bittersweet—sweet in knowing that you did it, and painful in knowing what it cost.

"A dream is expensive. It will cost you much. It will mean self-denial, for you must make your dream a priority. Whatever you give yourself to is what you become. It will determine if you give vent to the fire of the dream within you.

"Today we have a film that will depict an individual that went through many agonizing moments before he was able to do what burned deep within his subconscious mind. He abandoned a very lucrative medical career to become a writer. Let's listen to his own testimony."

After blacking out the room and positioning the screen into place, the teacher turned on the film. There appeared on the screen the picture of a man named A.J. Cronin, who talked about the turning point of his career.

He said, "I was 33 at the time, a doctor in the West End of London. I think I wasn't a bad doctor. My patients seemed to like me—not only the nice old ladies with nothing wrong with them who lived near the Park and paid handsomely for my cheerful bedside manner, but the cabbies, porters and deadbeats in the mews and back streets of Bayswater who paid nothing and often had a great deal wrong with them.

"Yet there was something...though I treated everything that came my way, read all the medical journals, attended scientific meetings, and even found time to take complex post-graduate diplomas...I wasn't quite sure of myself.

"One day I developed indigestion. After resisting my wife's entreaties for several weeks I went, casually, to consult a friendly colleague. I expected a bottle of bismuth and an invitation to bridge. I received instead the shock of my life—a sentence to six months' complete rest in the country on a milk diet. I had a gastric ulcer.

"The place of exile, chosen after excruciating contention, was a small farmhouse near the village of Tarbert in the Scottish Highlands. Imagine a lonely whitewashed steading set on a rain-drenched loch amid ferocious mountains rising into gray mist, with long-horned cattle, like elders of the kirk, sternly munching thistles in the foreground. That was Fyne Farm. Conceive of a harassed stranger in city clothes arriving with a pain in his middle and a box of peptonizing powders in his suitcase. That was me.

"Nothing is more agonizing to the active man than enforced idleness. A week of Fyne Farm drove me crazy. Debarred from all physical pursuits, I was reduced to feeding the chickens and learning to greet the disapproving cattle by their Christian names. Casting round desperately for something to do, I had a sudden idea. For years, at the back of my mind, I had nursed the vague illusion that I might write. Often, indeed, in unguarded moments, I had remarked to my wife: 'You know, I believe I could write a novel if I had time,' at which she would smile kindly across her knitting and murmur, 'Do you, dear?' and tactfully lead me back to talk of Johnnie Smith's whooping cough.

"Now as I stood on the shore of that desolate Highland loch I raised my voice in a surge of self-justification: 'By Heavens! This is my opportunity. Gastric ulcer or no gastric ulcer, I will write a novel.' Before I could change my mind I walked straight to the village and bought myself two dozen penny exercise books.

"Upstairs in my cold, clean bedroom was a scrubbed deal table and a very hard chair. Next morning I found myself in this chair, facing a new exercise book open upon the table, slowly becoming aware that, short of dog Latin prescriptions, I had never composed a significant phrase in all my life. It was a discouraging thought as I picked up my pen and gazed out of the window. Never mind, I would begin....Three hours later Mrs. Angus, the farmer's wife, called me to dinner. The page was still blank.

"As I went down to my milk and junket (they call this 'curds' in Tarbert), I felt a dreadful fool. I felt like the wretched poet in Daudet's Jack whose immortal masterpiece never progressed beyond its stillborn opening phrase: 'In a remote valley of the Pyrenees...' I recollected, rather grimly, the sharp advice with which my old schoolmaster had goaded me to action. 'Get it down!' he had said. 'If it stops in your head it will always be nothing. Get it down.' And so, after lunch, I went upstairs and began to get it down.

"Perhaps the tribulations of the next three months are best omitted. I had in my head, clear enough, the theme I wished to treat, the tragic record of a man's egoism and bitter pride. I even had the title of the book. But beyond these naive fundamentals I was lamentably unprepared. I had no pretensions to technique, no knowledge of style or form. I had never seen a thesaurus. The difficulty of simple statement staggered me. I spent hours looking for an adjective. I corrected and recorrected until the page looked like a spider's web, then I tore it up and started all over again.

"Yet once I had begun, the thing haunted me. My characters took shape, spoke to me, laughed, wept, excited me. When an idea struck me in the middle of the night I would get up, light a candle, and sprawl on the floor until I had translated it to paper. I was possessed by the very novelty of what I did. At first my rate of progress was some 800 labored words a day. By the end of the second month I was readily accomplishing 2000.

"Suddenly, when I was halfway through, the inevitable happened. A sudden desolation struck me like an avalanche. I asked myself: 'Why am I wearing myself out with this toil for which I am so preposterously ill-equipped? What is the use of it? I ought to be resting...conserving, not squandering my energies on this fantastic task.' I threw down my pen. Feverishly, I read over the first chapters which had just arrived in typescript from my secretary in London. I was appalled. Never, never had I seen such nonsense in all my life. No one would read it. I saw, finally, that I was a presumptuous lunatic, that all that I had written, all that I could ever write was wasted effort, sheer futility. I decided to abandon the whole thing. Abruptly, furiously, I bundled up the manuscript, went out and threw it in the ash can.

"Drawing a sullen satisfaction from my surrender, or, as I preferred to phrase it, my return to sanity, I went for a walk in the drizzling rain. Halfway down the loch shore I came upon old Angus, the farmer, patiently and laboriously ditching a patch of the bogged and peaty heath which made up the bulk of his hard-won little croft. As I drew near, he gazed up at me in some surprise: he knew of my intention and, with that inborn Scottish reverence for 'letters,' had tacitly approved it.

"When I told him what I had just done, and why, his weathered face slowly changed, his keen blue eyes, beneath misted sandy brows, scanned me with disappointment and a queer contempt. He was a silent man and it was long before he spoke. Even then his words were cryptic.

"'No doubt you're the one that's right, Doctor, and I'm the one that's wrong...' He seemed to look right to the bottom of me. 'My father ditched this bog all his days and never made a pasture. I've dug it all my days and I've never made a pasture. But pasture or no pasture,' he placed his foot dourly on the spade, 'I canna help but dig. For my father knew and I know that if you only dig enough a pasture can be made here.'

"I understood. I watched his dogged working figure, with rising anger and resentment. I was resentful because he had what I had not: a terrible stubbornness to see the job through at all costs, an unquenchable flame of resolution brought to the simplest, the most arid duties of life. And suddenly my trivial dilemma became magnified, transmuted, until it stood as a touchstone of all human conduct. It became the timeless problem of mortality—the comfortable retreat, or the arduous advance without prospect of reward.

"I tramped back to the farm, drenched, shamed, furious, and picked the soggy bundle from the ash can. I dried it in the kitchen oven. Then I flung it on the table and set to work again with a kind of frantic desperation. I lost myself in the ferociousness of my purpose. I would not be beaten, I would not give in. I wrote harder than ever. At last, toward the end of the third month, I wrote *finis*. The relief, the sense of emancipation, was unbelievable. I had kept my word. I had created a book. Whether it was good, bad or indifferent I did not care.

"I chose a publisher by the simple expedient of closing my eyes and pricking a catalogue with a pin. I dispatched the completed manuscript and promptly forgot about it.

"In the days which followed I gradually regained my health, and I began to chafe at idleness. I wanted to be back in harness.

"At last the date of my deliverance drew near. I went round the village saying good-bye to the simple folk who had become my friends. As I entered the post office, the postmaster presented me with a telegram—an urgent invitation to meet the publisher. I took it straight away and showed it, without a word to John Angus.

"The novel I had thrown away was chosen by the Book Society, dramatized and serialized, translated into 19 languages, bought by Hollywood. It has sold, to date, some three million copies. It has altered my life radically, beyond my wildest dreams...and all because of a timely lesson in the grace of perseverance."[1]

The teacher turned the film off and we all sat there impressed and challenged. She proceeded to talk about it.

"The book that he was referring to in the film is called *Hatter's Castle*. It caused a sensation to put it mildly. This low time in his life was a turning point in his career. The loneliness that he felt in the months preceding his success were days that he does not even like to talk about. It was because of something some people would refer as to a 'setback' that really helped him to pursue his shadowy dream. And even then, it was not easy doing something he had never done before. He had only a dream as a foundation."

As she stopped talking and stillness entered the room, Jonathan thought, "How many dreams are in ash cans? How many people couldn't stand the despair and loneliness?"

She interrupted his thoughts by gently opening a cupboard door and getting out the assignment for the day. She handed the five their work and waved good-bye as she exited out the back door.

"Well, if A.J. Cronin can write a book in 1931 and be successful, I can also get my dream out of the ash can and bring it to pass," Jonathan said aloud.

John echoed all of their thoughts, "That was one of the most powerful films. It will stay forever inside my consciousness."

The five were all deeply moved as they approached the work she had given them for their assignment. After working awhile Jonathan got up from his seat and slowly walked around the room looking at posters and other inspirational material before leaving out the back door. He found a pathway so he followed it. It led to a small lake where there were ducks and other wild birds dipping and bathing. He sat down and watched them lazily, feeling very relaxed.

It was not long until his stomach told him it was time to eat. Walking back to the camp he resolved that the Scottish farmer would not outdo him. He went straight to the dining hall where everyone was already eating, and what a spread it was...roast, carrots, potatoes, gravy and biscuits with homemade jam.

It was a treat when the President walked in. Everyone clapped and cheered as he came over and sat down to eat with them. After they ate, the tables were cleared, and the five listened to Mr. Theodore talk and tell stories. It was an undisputed feeling that he was a very inspirational man! He talked about great men that gave the world something.

He said, "Do not give up easy, boys! It was Beethoven who was unsurpassed in his painstaking fidelity to his music. Hardly a bar of his was not written and rewritten at least a dozen times. Michelangelo's *Last Judgment,* one of the twelve master paintings of the ages, was the product of eight years' unremitting toil. Over 2,000 studies of it were found among his papers.

Leonardo Da Vinci worked on *The Last Supper* for ten years, often so absorbed he forgot to eat for whole days. Westinghouse was treated as a mild lunatic by most railroad executives. 'Stopping a train by wind! The man's crazy!' they would say. Yet he persevered and finally sold the air-brake idea."

Listening to the President always inspired the five to reach for greater things. They all talked among themselves after he bid them good-night until finally they made their way to their cottages.

Later that night after Jonathan went to bed he could still hear the old farmer's words ringing in his ears, "For my father knew and I know that if you only dig enough a pasture can be made here."

He thought, "The hard work, the loneliness, the long hours doesn't matter; it's the results that count. The glow of a job finished, of a dream realized, is what is important."

As he rolled over to go to sleep, he could not help but think that this was just the beginning of the rest of his life!

14

FAITH & CONFIDENCE

*A*s the sun shone through the window bathing the room with a sunny glow, Jonathan greeted the day with a smile. "Three more days and I'll be gone from this place," he shouted to the sun.

The knowledge of this filled him with mixed emotions—he was glad because he was excited to pursue his dream again, but sad because he had to leave such an inspirational place. He realized his whole life would change; he would never be the same again.

Wanting to smell the fresh air, he went to the door and opened it. There was Benjamin walking up the pathway towards him. "Good morning," Jonathan sang out.

"A very good morning to you," he responded.

There seemed to be a feeling of exhilaration that filled the atmosphere.

"You will love today's lesson," Benjamin said. "This lesson is always one of the favorites."

"Well, I'm ready for it," Jonathan said. "I love the way these teachers cause my brain to expand."

Benjamin chuckled and said, "It is rewarding to the teachers to have such a fertile mind as yours, and to know that one day the dream that you cherish will soar and fly."

Waving at Benjamin as he walked away, Jonathan said, "See you in a little while."

Later when Benjamin came back they started walking to where the lesson would be held that day. They walked up to a clean, immaculate building. Jonathan opened the door, bid Benjamin good-day and went inside, finding a seat near his friends. It was a very inspirational room, different from the ones he had been in before. The room was flooded with sunshine from the many windows on either side of the room.

The teacher walked in with a big smile on his face that exuded faith and assurance. He was a tall man with a straight spine and sparkling eyes. He said, "Today our subject is Faith and Confidence."

He then unrolled a large laminated canvas and began to talk. "While you've been here you were told that you would be discussing Abraham Lincoln's Creed. Today is the day.

"You must believe in something or you will never amount to anything. Of course, your belief must be in something positive or your belief will destroy you. Lincoln's creed is very positive because the underlying force of his beliefs is his faith in the eternal God. Let's talk about it and go over each point."

Each of the five took turns reading it as he highlighted each number with his pointer.

ABRAHAM LINCOLN'S CREED

1. *I believe in God, the Almighty Ruler of Nations, our great and good and merciful Maker, our Father in*

Heaven, who notes the fall of a sparrow, and numbers the hairs of our heads.

2. *I believe in His eternal truth and justice.*

3. *I recognize the sublime truth announced in the Holy Scriptures and proven by all history that those nations only are blest whose God is the Lord.*

4. *I believe that it is the duty of nations as well as of men to own their dependence upon the overruling power of God, and to invoke the influence of His Holy Spirit; to confess their sins and transgressions in humble sorrow, yet with assured hope that genuine repentance will lead to mercy and pardon.*

5. *I believe that it is meet and right to recognize and confess the presence of the Almighty Father equally in our triumphs and in the sorrows which we may justly fear are a punishment inflicted upon us for our presumptuous sins to the needful end of our reformation.*

6. *I believe that the Bible is the best gift which God has ever given men. All the good from the Saviour of the world is communicated to us through this book.*

7. *I believe the will of God prevails. Without Him all human reliance is vain. Without the assistance of that Divine Being I cannot succeed. With that assistance I cannot fail.*

8. *Being a humble instrument in the hands of our Heavenly Father, I desire that all my works and acts may be according to His will; and that it may be so, I give thanks to the Almighty, and seek His aid.*

9. *I have a solemn oath registered in Heaven to finish the work I am in; in full view of my responsibility to my God, with malice toward none, with charity for all; with firmness in the right as God gives me to see the right...* [1]

As they finished reading the creed, the force of Abraham Lincoln's beliefs permeated the room. The air was thick with a powerful faith. After a few minutes' silence, the teacher continued to teach. It seemed that he was set on fire with what he was saying.

"Without faith and confidence, you cannot reach your goals. These are the most important elements. Faith will take nothing and believe it into existence. It grabs hold when there is not an ounce of substance to behold.

"Faith causes you to have INITIATIVE. It will adopt the attitude of Admiral Perry in his long struggle to reach the North Pole. He said, 'I will find a way or make one.' Nothing stands in the way of this kind of faith.

"It also will be the fuel for AMBITION. Ambition is the spirit that makes man struggle with destiny. Faith without ambition is like a ship without a rudder. There must be a cause for faith to be able to germinate in.

"Faith without DETERMINATION cannot achieve anything. It is not enough to believe, it must stick in there until the job is accomplished.

"Anne Sullivan, the famous teacher of Helen Keller, had the ingredient of faith in working with her pupil. When she arrived at the Keller home and saw the wild, unruly five-year-old animal, whom no one could understand or control, she determined that she would be the one to help the little girl. With confidence and faith she brought about a miracle and changed the direction of Helen's life. It was her faith, ambition, initiative, and determination that brought light into Helen's darkness.

"Helen Keller stated in her book, *The Story of My Life,* the following words that say it well: 'Have you ever been at sea in a dense fog, when it seemed as if a tangible white darkness shut you in, and the great ship, tense and anxious, groped her way toward the shore with plummet and sounding-line, and you waited with beating heart for something to happen? I was like that ship before my education began, only I was without compass or sounding-line, and had no way of knowing how near the harbour was. "Light! Give me light!" was the wordless cry of my soul, and the light of love shone on me that very hour.

"'I felt approaching footsteps. I stretched out my hand as I supposed it to be my mother. Someone took it, and I was caught up and held close in the arms of her who had come to reveal all things to me, and more than all things else, to love me.'[2]

"Anne Sullivan's faith in her pupil brought her out of her darkness, and she in turn helped bring many others out of their dark depression."

The teacher paused and pulled out a tiny seed from a small cabinet before proceeding. "This seed is a mustard seed. When Christ walked on the earth, He told His disciples that if they had faith the size of a grain of mustard seed nothing would be impossible to them. He went on to say that they could say unto a mountain, 'Be removed,' and it would remove itself. He showed them that faith believes that the impossible can be done.

"A seed smaller than a pinhead planted in the ground produces a great tree. In the same way, a small thought germinates in your brain and produces a great work. The element of faith in the rain to come and the ground to yield forth produces the tree.

"Just as the earth spins around its axis, an imaginary line that connects the North and South poles, all dreams spin around an axis, which is faith. Faith cannot be seen, but it is there; it is an integral part. All dreams are anchored by this ingredient. This anchor also gives it the freedom to soar and become. Let's look at a man who lived with that ingredient most of his life."

The teacher darkened the room, lowered the screen, and turned on the projector, showing a man named Johann Sebastian Bach. The film began:

"Johann Sebastian Bach is considered the greatest genius of baroque music. Although he touched a world with his music, his life was not always easy.

"He was born in Eisenach, Germany, on March 21, 1685. His parents died before he was ten. He then lived with his older brother who taught him to play the clavichord and harpsichord.

"In 1721, he married Anna Magdalena Wilcken, a professional singer. They had thirteen children. He moved to Leipiz in 1723 and spent the rest of his life there. He became the director of music for St. Thomas' School, which provided music for churches in the city.

"The people of Bach's time appreciated him as an organist, but generally ignored his compositions. His complete works fill about sixty volumes, but only nine or ten of his compositions were published during his lifetime. The people of his time considered his complex baroque compositions too elaborate. "About 1740, at the age of 55, he began to have serious eye trouble, and in his last years he was nearly blind."

When the film was finished, the teacher summarized it by showing what drove Bach on in spite of the odds. "The death of his parents, the huge responsibility of feeding and clothing thirteen children and the lack of people's approval did not discourage him. He believed in what he was doing. The faith in his dream drove him on. People's applause did not matter; the thing that mattered was that it was inside of him and he had to get it down on paper. He believed enough in what he was doing to preserve it even though it was not respected so much during his lifetime."

With those words he closed his notebook and the challenging lesson was over for the day.

"Thank you for a great lesson," the five spoke as one.

"It's an important one. It will take you through when nothing else will. Do not ever forget it," the teacher responded.

He then gave them some more material to study and with a wave of his hand was gone. Again they sat and tried to soak up everything that had been presented to them. Jonathan remembered Benjamin had already given to him and the other four *Abraham Lincoln's Creed*. Now he knew in which chapter to place it.

Awhile later, after studying, he walked quickly to the cottage and searched around until he found it and inserted it into his notebook. For the rest of the day he just took it easy meditating and digesting everything so as not to lose any of it.

The Dreamers

That night after dinner, the five played Rook until almost midnight. Later stumbling sleepily into bed, Jonathan fell right to sleep.

15

INCLUDE GOD

The next morning after breakfast, Jonathan followed Benjamin to a small room that looked like a miniature chapel. As Benjamin walked away, Jonathan entered into the dim interior where restful inspirational music was playing in the background. He sat down and soaked up the peace that seemed to permeate the room. While sitting there, his four friends walked in looking as if they had just awakened. He stood up and was talking to them when they heard a door open in the back. Looking toward it they saw a man with a cheerful countenance motioning for them to come into his office. As the five walked towards him, he said, "Today is a great day to be alive!"

When introductions were made and they found out his name was Paul, Jonathan shook his hand with feeling, saying, "Almost two weeks ago I didn't feel like life was worth living, but this school has helped to change my mind." He looked at the others and they nodded assent to what he had just said.

Paul smiled and said, "People are influenced by what they listen to and by what they read. If they will change their thoughts, it will help change their world and direction."

The five looked around the room at the many pictures of men and women who had been successful in life. Their names were at the bottom of each picture, along with a brief explanation of their successes. Some of them were well known, others were not. There was an older lady who was bent over and it was apparent she had been a hard worker. The inscription under her name simply said, "She was successful because she gave her life to caring about the orphans. She brought love, laughter and inspiration to lives that were dark, dreary, and hopeless."

Paul, noticing the five looking at it, said, "To be successful you do not have to have your name in lights. The whole world does not have to know who you are.

"To be totally successful in life you must include God in your life. After awhile even fame and attainment might sour, but if you include God in your plans, you will always have a reason to live."

He paused and pointed to an antique-looking book and said, "There is one book He gave to mankind which you never want to be without, and that is the Holy Bible. It has guided men and women successfully down through the ages. For instance read what God spoke to Joshua, a very successful leader of the Israelite people. Here, you read it, Jonathan."

Jonathan looked down at the well-worn Bible and read out loud, "This book of the law shall not depart out of thy mouth, but thou shalt meditate therein day and night, that thou mayest observe to do according to all that is written therein: for then thou shalt make thy way prosperous, and then thou shalt have good success" (Joshua 1:8).

The five stood there in silence as the words sank into their consciousness. Then Paul began to speak. "Most successful men, women, and colleges in the past included God in their plans. One man in particular that I like to talk about was R.G. LeTourneau. He was a high school dropout back in the early 1900's, but became a millionaire many times over. He could not seem to find direction until he included God into his plans. His favorite saying was, 'By accepting God as your partner, no limit can be placed on what can be achieved.'[1]

"He went from a small-time builder of earth moving equipment to one of the largest in the world. During World War II it was his organization that built over fifty percent of the earth-moving equipment used in combat. His attitude propelled him into success.

"He said, 'I've read that Alexander wept because he had no more worlds to conquer. I've heard young engineers in my own shop complain that they've arrived too late to make any major discoveries. That's all nonsense. All inventors stand on the shoulders of the inventors who have gone before them, and the bigger the inventor, the higher the newcomers can stand.'"[2]

Paul continued talking earnestly about Mr. LeTourneau. "For years when he would get an inspiration or idea, people would call him crazy. He believed in his dreams and hunches and followed them anyway. At the age of 70 he was still going strong inventing a new machine that would move 150 tons of dirt instead of 75.

"He said in his autobiography, 'There was only one thing lacking in the newspaper reports and articles in the technical journals after the writers and photographers had covered my first public demonstration of the new 150-ton earth mover. No one called me crazy. I was even treated with respect, sometimes

123

overwhelmingly so. Some called me a genius without once qualifying it by adding the adjective *eccentric.*"[3]

The teacher stopped talking while the five let his words sink into their brains. Then he began teaching again. "Another inventor, Benjamin Franklin, invented more things than any other person. He was a man who lived deliberately and purposefully. He also made the choice to include God in his plans. Listen to the speech he made to the assembly in the summer of 1787 when the representatives met in Philadelphia to write the Constitution of the United States. After they had struggled for several weeks, 81-year-old Benjamin Franklin rose and addressed the troubled convention.

Paul switched on a tape player, and as he did a re-creation of Franklin's speech filled the room, transporting the five back to over 200 years before. The speech was straightforward, but convincing. They listened carefully to the words of the great statesman:

"Mr. President, the small progress we have made after four or five weeks close attendance and continual reasoning with each other—our different sentiments on almost every question, several of the last producing as many noes as ayes—is, methinks, a melancholy proof of the imperfection of the human understanding. We indeed seem to feel our own want of political wisdom, since we have been running about to search of it. We have gone back to ancient history for models of government, and examined the different forms of those republics which, having been formed with seeds of their own dissolution, now no longer exist. And we have viewed modern states all round Europe, but find none of their constitutions suitable to our circumstances.

"In this situation of this Assembly, groping as it were in the dark to find political truth, and scarce able to distinguish it when presented to us, how has it happened, Sir, that we have not hitherto once thought of humbly applying to the Father of lights, to illuminate our understandings? In the beginning of the contest with Great Britain, when we were sensible of danger, WE HAD DAILY PRAYER IN THIS ROOM FOR THE DIVINE PROTECTION. OUR PRAYERS, SIR, WERE HEARD, AND THEY WERE GRACIOUSLY ANSWERED.

"All of us who are engaged in the struggle must have observed frequent instances of superintending Providence in our favor. To that kind of Providence we owe this happy opportunity of consulting in peace on the means of establishing our future national felicity. And have we now forgotten that powerful friend? Or do we imagine that we no longer need his assistance? I have lived, Sir, a long time, and the longer I live the more convincing proofs I see of this truth—THAT GOD GOVERNS IN THE AFFAIRS OF MEN.

"And if a sparrow cannot fall to the ground without his notice, is it probable that an empire can rise without his aid? We have been assured, Sir, in the sacred writings that, 'except the Lord build the house they labor in vain that build it.' I firmly believe this; and I also believe that without his concurring aid we shall succeed in this political building no better than the builders of Babel. We shall be divided by our little partial local interests; our projects will be confounded; and we ourselves shall become a reproach and by-word down to future ages. And what is worse, mankind may hereafter from this unfortunate instance, despair of establishing government by human wisdom, and leave it to chance, war and conquest.

"I therefore beg leave to move—that henceforth prayers imploring the assistance of Heaven, and its blessings on our deliberations, be held in this Assembly every morning before we proceed to business, and that one or more of the clergy of this city be requested to officiate in that service."[4]

When the tape was finished the teacher handed each young man a sheet of paper and said, "Not only did the men who were involved in the forming of the Constitution ask for God's assistance, but so were the men who organized America's first colleges. Read these facts about some of the presidents' views."

They went around the circle reading out loud.

John read, "Testimony from Harvard: The first college, HARVARD, was established for 'Christ the Church.' In his bequest of the first large gift of what is now Harvard University, John Harvard said: 'Let every student be plainly instructed and earnestly pressed to consider well the main ends of his life and studies; to know God and Jesus Christ, which is eternal life, and therefore to lay Christ in the bottom as the only foundation of all knowledge and learning and see that the Lord only giveth wisdom. Let everyone seriously set himself by prayer in secret to see Christ as Lord and Master.'[5]

"Above Harvard gates are etched today these words: 'After God had carried us safe to New England, and we had built our houses, provided necessities for our livelihood, reared convenient places for God's worship, and settled the civil government; one of the next thing we longed for, and looked after was to advance learning and perpetuate it to posterity; dreading to leave an illiterate ministry to the churches, when our present ministers shall lie in the dust.'"

Tim then took over reading. "Harvard's Christ-centered rules and precepts adopted in 1646 read:

(1) Everyone shall consider the main end of his life and study to know God and Jesus Christ which is eternal.

(2) Seeing the Lord giveth wisdom every one shall seriously by prayer in secret seek wisdom of him.

(3) Everyone shall so exercise himself in reading the Scriptures twice a day that they be ready to give an account of the proficiency therein, both in theocratical observation of languages and logic and in practical and spiritual truths...

"And thus 52% of the 17th century Harvard graduates became ministers."[6]

Michael read the Testimony from Yale: "Yale, from its beginning in 1701 was more conservative. In 1825, a Yale gospel group traveled around the country on evangelistic ministry. Timothy Dwight, president from 1795 to 1817 advised the class of 1814: 'Christ is the only, the true, the living way of success to God. Give up yourselves therefore to him, with a cordial confidence, and the great work of life is done.'"[7]

Michael continued reading the testimony from Columbia. "When King's College, now Columbia University, opened in 1754, the following was part of an advertisement published for the school: 'The chief thing that is aimed at in this college is to teach and engage children to know God in Jesus Christ.'"[8]

Joe then took over the reading. "Testimony from Princeton: Princeton in the early days insisted that the faculty be 'convinced of the necessity of religious experience for salvation.' John Witherspoon, first president of Princeton said: 'Cursed be all learning that is contrary to the cross of Christ. Cursed be all learning that is not coincident with the cross of

Christ. Cursed be all learning that is not subservient to the cross of Christ.'"9

When they finished reading, the five agreed that the great land of the United States of America could trace her roots back to men, women, and presidents who had included God in their plans. Her faith was emblazoned on every penny in America: "In God We Trust."

The teacher then opened the antique book again and read slowly Matthew 19:26: "With God all things are possible."

He then, like all the other teachers, gave the five a stack of reading and work assignments and left them alone to study. For a while they did not read, but just stared at the pictures of all the people on the wall, while thinking of what they had just heard and read. They were almost in a state of shock.

Joe voiced it the best. He said, "To think that our country had such roots! Don't you feel a little cheated when you think about young men our age that grew up with such a value system?"

Tim joined in, "No wonder the kids did not need drugs, immorality, and alcohol back then. They had a God to believe in, someone they could trust."

After talking awhile the five settled down to some more serious reading about men and women that included God in their life and also some that challenged God. The five agreed that they would rather believe than challenge, especially after reading some of the things that happened to the challengers.

When Jonathan finally left the room and was walking back to his cottage he felt a sense of destiny pervading the atmosphere. He walked inside, stretched out on the bed and did some serious thinking.

That evening the President was at dinner again. Jonathan finally got up the courage to ask him a question that had been on his mind since the day's class. Not knowing exactly how to say it, he just blurted it out, "How come this generation shies away from God, when most of our forefathers included God in their lives? Many of our presidents prayed and talked about God openly. It worked for them, why do we think it will not work for us?"

The President looked thoughtful before answering. He said, "Jonathan, most of our country believed in God until there came what is called The Age of Reason among us. Men started questioning and reasoning as to the existence of God. This was, of course, after we had settled, established, and were doing quite well financially. Thomas Paine was one of the writers of that day. He was an immigrant to America in 1787. He leaped from obscurity to fame by writing brilliantly on freedom, but he made a fatal mistake when he wrote *The Age of Reason*, which scoffed at Christianity.

"In fact these were his words: 'This will destroy the Bible. Within 100 years, Bibles will be found only in museums or in musty corners of second-hand bookstores.'

"His book was published in London in 1794, but it brought him so much misery and loneliness that he once said, 'I would give worlds, if I had them, if *The Age of Reason* had never been written.'

"Of course, he died lonely and a bedridden invalid in 1809, but the Bible remained a best-seller."

The President looked around at the five and said, "It does not matter who speaks against God. God will always be, and He will have the last word. My advice to you young men is to include God in your lives as Abraham Lincoln, George Washington, and many other great successful men and women did. It is the happiest way because it is the right way."

He bid the five good-night and after he left they had a lively discussion about the day's lesson.

৵৶

Meanwhile, back at the cottage about four hours later, as Jonathan got ready for bed, he determined that God was going to be included in his life. With that decision he closed his eyes and slept peacefully.

16

OVERCOMING OBSTACLES

onathan woke up to the sound of a motor running outside. He looked out the window and became excited upon discovering that it was his car being driven by Benjamin. Hurriedly he dressed and ran to open the front door, greeting Benjamin who had turned the motor off and was walking towards him with the keys, saying, "I knew you'd be thrilled to see your car all fixed and ready to go again. The mechanic just brought it back, so I brought it over immediately."

Jonathan stammering with words and overcome by emotion, said, "Well, I don't know how to thank you enough. You have been so kind to me since I've been here. You've been a real friend, one I'll never forget."

Benjamin smiled and said, "Thank you, Jonathan. I'll always count you as my friend also."

Then looking at his watch, he said, "We're running late today. Stay here, I'm bringing you a special breakfast this morning."

Jonathan went outside and ran his hand over the newly repaired car and whistled a happy tune. While he was checking everything, Benjamin came walking back from the direction of the dining hall. It looked like he had outdone himself. He had a tray loaded with goodies.

"What's the occasion?" Jonathan asked.

"Your last day here. Remember?" Benjamin answered.

"Yes, I guess I will be leaving this evening," he said reluctantly.

"What's the matter? You don't want to go?" asked Benjamin.

"It's not that I don't want to go. It's just that this has been such an inspirational place and I've made some good friends here. It will be hard to leave."

"But it won't be forever," said Benjamin. "Now that you know we are here and have gone through the course, you can come back and visit us again."

Taking the tray of food inside and setting it on the table, Jonathan sat down and ate a very delicious breakfast. A short while later when Benjamin arrived back at the cottage, he was ready to go.

Benjamin led Jonathan towards what looked like a miniature obstacle course. They went through several difficult maneuvers and then started climbing up a rope ladder into a large tree where there was a room built among the branches. Jonathan thought, "This is the strangest classroom I've ever seen," but said, "Well, I always did want a tree house, so I'll just imagine this is it."

Benjamin was already climbing back down and was motioning for him to go on inside, saying, "Go enjoy your tree house."

Jonathan heard him chuckling as he reached the ground, and turned to go inside, but when he tried to open the door, it was locked. He called to Benjamin, but he was already gone. After waiting a few minutes he decided to go back down the rope ladder. As his foot touched the first rung of the ladder, the door opened.

He looked with shock into the face of a little old shriveled man who laughed uproariously and said, "Yes, you wondered how I got up here. Well, I may be old and shriveled, but I am still agile in mind and body. I can keep up with the best of them. Come on in here, boy, and let's begin our lesson. You are the last one to show up here today. The others are inside waiting for you."

Jonathan began to feel that the day's lesson was going to be an enjoyable one because of the man's sparkling personality that was hidden behind the exterior of his face. It reminded him of an old apple doll his grandmother had made.

"I didn't mean to be rude by looking shocked," he said, "but it is unusual to see someone your age teaching up in a class-room in the trees."

"It always shocks everyone," the teacher said, "but that makes the lesson more effective. For, you see, our lesson is about overcoming obstacles. That is why there were so many obstacles placed in the way. Then when you got here, the last thing you expected to see was a dried-up little old man."

He walked over to a stereo and placed a tape inside and beautiful music filled the room. After listening for awhile, he turned it off and began to talk.

"You have heard about the man that wrote this music since you've been here, but we need to talk about him some more. Beethoven was born in 1770 into a home of poverty with a drunken father. He lived a hard life and at the age of 22 left home and went to Vienna where he was welcomed with open arms into the musical society. His music was different and strange; it was moving and caused people to weep as they listened.

"He was a hard worker. He had learned responsibility as a small child. Especially at the age of 17, when his mother died and he had to shoulder the obligation of providing for his two younger brothers and his drunken father.

"He worked at his performance and his composing. In 1796, Beethoven scribbled on the margin of his sketchbook with his carpenter pencil these words that drove him on: 'Courage! Despite all the weaknesses of the body, my spirit shall rule! Here I am 25 years old. This year must bring out the complete man.'

"Just a few years later, in 1800, he was overtaken with the curse of deafness. He tried to hide it from the public hoping that he would be helped by the doctors. As time went on he was torn between suicide and the humiliation of failure in the face of his enemies.

"At the age of 31, he retreated to a little town called Aeiligenstadt away from the fun-loving Vienna. He wrote of his deafness, 'I AM RESOLVED TO RISE ABOVE EVERY OBSTACLE.'[1]

"Because of his deafness, he was forced into composition and less performance. By the end of 1809, he had finished six symphonies, the opera fidelio, fifteen piano sonatas, ten quartets, seven sonatas for two instruments, six overtures, five concertos, a sextet, a ballet, an oratorio, a quintet, a mass, and numerous songs, variations and other compositions.

"He was often asked to move on to new quarters because he banged on the piano so loudly and at odd hours. Since he could not hear, the loud vibrations communicated to him what he needed to hear.

"In 1824, Beethoven finished one of his greatest works, the Ninth Symphony, Opus 125. It is also called the Choral Symphony, for in the fourth movement singers join the orchestra, and a grand chorus sings the happy theme from Schiller's *Ode to Joy*. He worked six years on this effort.

"The tragic thing about it was that Beethoven could not hear it. On the night of its performance at the Karnthnerthor Hall, the Symphony was received enthusiastically and a wild burst of applause filled the place. Beethoven heard neither his great symphony nor the applause. One of the soloists pulled the sleeve of his coat and turned him away from the pages of the score to face the wildly clapping audience. It was a touching scene, for it was obvious that Beethoven was stone-deaf. Half blind and deaf, he was giving the world something to cheer about.

"Anton Schindler, from Vienna, wrote about another one of Beethoven's masterpieces: 'Never did so great a work of art as is the Missa Solemnis see its creation under more adverse circumstances.'"[2]

The teacher paused and all the historical facts about Beethoven made Jonathan think, "If he did that with deafness and being half blind, I have no excuse."

His thoughts were interrupted as the teacher began to talk again. "Your dreams will bring pressure, hardship and adversity, but that is the time to press on and overcome the obstacles, not to give up. A few days ago in your lesson you studied the life of Winston Churchill. He was a man who overcame many hardships. He started off in life without much promise, a slow learner. He lost the first election for which he ran. He recovered from pneumonia, strokes, and other physical ailments. He waded through fiery wars and political arenas. He won, he lost, but always bounced back a winner. He beat the odds that were against him and forged ahead to victory."

The teacher talked rapidly and with excitement. He walked over to the wall and pulled down a picture of Helen Keller. He said, "We cannot talk about overcoming obstacles without talking about this woman," the teacher declared.

"She was blind, deaf, and dumb. She was like a little animal, untamed. Anne Sullivan, her teacher, broke this prison in which she was encased. She taught her to communicate through touch. She taught her to read and write in Braille. A special typewriter was made for her on which she did all her writing. She wrote several books and one of them was entitled *Optimism,* a strange title for someone who had many things against her.

"Until she was ten years old, she could only talk using sign language. She decided she would learn to speak, and took lessons from a teacher of the deaf. By the time she was sixteen, she could speak well enough to go to preparatory school and to college. She chose Radcliffe, from which she graduated with honors in 1904.

"In her book, *The Story of My Life,* she tells of the difficulties she found there. She wrote, 'There are days when the close attention I must give to details chafes my spirit, and the thought that I must spend hours reading a few chapters, while in the world without other girls are laughing and singing...makes me rebellious; but I soon recover my buoyancy and laugh the discontent out of my heart. For, after all, every one who wishes to gain true knowledge must climb the Hill Difficulty alone, and since there is no royal road to the summit, I must zigzag it in my own way. I slip back many times, I fall, I stand still, I run against the edge of hidden obstacles, I lose my temper and find it again and keep it better, I trudge on, I gain a little, I feel encouraged, I get more eager and climb higher and begin to see the widening horizon. Every struggle is a victory. One more effort and I reach the luminous cloud, the blue depths of the sky, the uplands of my desire.' [3]

"After college, she was not content to help only herself. She wanted to expand her world and help others. She became interested in bettering conditions for the blind in underdeveloped and war-ravaged countries. She lectured in their behalf in more than 25 countries on the five major continents. Her books went with her and were translated into more than 50 languages.

"During World War II, she worked with soldiers who had been blinded in the war. Wherever she appeared, she brought new courage to millions of blind people. She was a challenge and inspiration to millions of people who were not blind."

The teacher stopped talking and looked straight at the five. He said, "Ideas come like a flash. Dreams are like tight-fitting gloves—they hug the consciousness of a person. They become interwoven with the core of an individual. They are never forgotten. A song, play, conversation, and many other things become fuel for the dream. You can either squash, ignore, or dampen the dream, or ignite and encourage it.

"You are leaving here this evening. You are not blind, deaf, dumb, crippled, or paralyzed. You are whole! You have all your faculties working for you. Do not let the security of these things take away from producing. Sometimes when it's too comfortable there is a tendency to settle in and exist and not perform. Put a burr under your own saddle; do not wait for something terrible to happen."

The teacher pointed his finger at them and said, "You are young. Go forth from here, believing that you can do it and lean heavily upon the God of the universe. He can do all things and He will help you, but He will not do your work for you."

With that final bit of admonition, he exited out the door with the speed of a younger man. As Jonathan thought about the lesson, his brain swelled with the impact of all that he had learned.

He also recalled the day he had taken a walk in the woods and felt like he was being followed. It came to him in a flash of inspiration that it was not an actual person following him, but the shadowy influence of what he had been before the crash.

As he stood up, the others stood up. They took one more look around the room and then left out the door. The rope ladder was waiting for them just as it had waited for other would-be dreamers. When they got to the bottom of the ladder they found Benjamin waiting for them.

"We'll go out a different way than the way we came in," he said. "You will not want to go through all that again."

"I was just thinking the same thing," Jonathan responded.

When they came into the clearing where the main camp stood, there was a surprise waiting for them. All the teachers, the President and a few other people were there. They had wanted to come and see the five before they left.

Jonathan sensed the other four were touched as deeply as he was. To think that they would care for them like this and take the time to say good-bye to young men that had fallen in on them at a minute's notice was heartwarming. They had nothing personal invested in all this. Their gesture of love and concern spoke volumes to the five.

To top it all off the President moved towards them and handed each of them a package and said, "We wanted to give you something to remember us by and to give you inspiration in the days to come."

Taking the packages, they opened them while the others watched. With tears in his eyes, Jonathan drew out a beautiful eagle that had its wings spread as if in flight.

"Thank you," he said huskily. "Your faith in me will keep me going. I will never forget you, for you have helped restore my dream."

For a few minutes everything was charged with emotion as Tim, Joe, John and Michael said their thanks, and then Benjamin said, "Come and eat. You have a few hours of driving in front of you."

"How do you know we have a few hours?" Jonathan asked.

"Well, we saw the registration with your address and found that you live three hours away. Since you have offered to take the others with you to bus stops and other towns on the way, you will have more than three hours' driving."

"Nothing escapes your eye, does it, Benjamin?" Jonathan joked with him.

"I guess nothing that's important," Benjamin countered.

They all walked together the rest of the way to the dining hall. When they arrived there, the cook had baked a large decorated cake with the names of the five written on it. He had outdone himself. It truly was a memorable occasion.

After eating, the five went back to their cottages to pick up their notebooks and a few other things. They did not have much to take with them, but what they did have was going to change their lives.

Meeting in the clearing where the car was parked, they put their things in the trunk of the car, including the important notebooks called *The Dreamer's Treasure Chest*. As they were saying their final good-byes to Benjamin, they heard a cry and looked up towards the sky. There above the tree was the beautiful eagle they had watched previously. It seemed he flew down and dipped his wing toward them as if saying good-bye. They experienced a strange sensation watching that eagle. For the last time they shook Benjamin's hand and said good-bye. Jonathan climbed into the driver's seat while the others filled the other seats, and with a final wave they were gone.

They drove up through the beautiful forest along the winding mountain road until they came to the main road from which Jonathan had crashed. He slowed down and viewed it with mixed emotions, thinking, "When I enter the valley this time, I will be a changed man. My old ideas and thoughts have been replaced by proven theories. I will never give up, but will join the men and women who have achieved. Yes, I will be a winner!"

Aloud he told his four friends, "I am going to give myself to making my dream come true. If changes are needed, I will change. Look out, world, here I come. I'm going to win!"

Tim, Michael, John, and Joe joined in, saying much the same thing. With that affirmation, Jonathan pulled on to the main highway and drove into the future, while all were silent in the car as the five were all lost in their own thoughts.

EPILOGUE

*T*he young men in this book could be you. Maybe you have "crashed" in your pursuit of a dream. As their dream was tarnished, so yours could be.

Have you said, "It's too difficult. The sacrifice is not worth it. I'll just be normal, just exist"? Then once in awhile in an unexpected moment does your dream shine through the clutter of life, and in your heart you experience a moment of anguish as you think about what might have been?

It is not too late. Learn from the lessons they learned. Get up and do, for whatever you give yourself to is what you become. If you are young, great. If you are middle-aged, great. If you are older, great. Many great works were given to the world by older men and women.

The important thing is to start doing something about it again. Never give up! Do it today. Let it sing once more in your heart and brain. Let it give you an excitement you have not known for awhile. Let your music be heard by the world. Give your best and the best will return to you. Honor your Creator by doing something with what he inspired you with. Do not let it die, but let it live!

Nothing is impossible to him that believeth. Keep working and believing that it shall be done! Always remember that many who succeeded in life passed through many heartbreaking struggles before they arrived at the their destination of success. Dreams are not born of laziness, lack of ambition, or indifference. They are fired with enthusiasm and persistence.

Look not on what you do not have, but on what you have. Edgar Allan Poe, considered to be a literary genius, was an orphan before he was three, kicked out of school, suffered from poverty, but yet he gave the world articles, essays, brilliant criticism, poetry, and detective stories.

Another boy was so slow to learn to talk that his parents thought him abnormal and his teachers called him a "misfit." His classmates avoided him and seldom invited him to play with them. He failed his first college entrance exam in Zurich, Switzerland. A year later he tried again. In time he became world famous as a scientist. His name: Albert Einstein.

Do not give up, because quitters never win and winners never quit! You can do it one minute at a time until it becomes substance. As Henry David Thoreau said so many years ago, **"Men were born to succeed, not to fail."**

NOTES

Chapter 1

[1] Collected and edited by Burton Egbert Stevenson, *Poems of American History*, (New York, NY: Houghton Muflin Co., 1908).

Chapter 3

[1] Brooks Atkinson, *Walden and Other Writings of Henry David Thoreau*, (New York, NY: The Modern Library, Random House, 1937).

Chapter 4

[1] The World Book Encyclopedia, Vol. 16, (Chicago, IL: Field Enterprises Educational Corp., 1968), pp 425-426.

[2] David Wallechinsky & Irving Wallace, *The People's Almanac #2*, (New York, NY: Bantam Books, 1978).

[3] Ibid

[4-9] William F. Keefe, *The Rubber Man*, Childcraft, The How and Why Library, (Chicago, IL: Field Enterprises Educational Corp., 1978), pp 71-75.

Chapter 5

[1] Phillips Russell, *Benjamin Franklin, The First Civilized American*, (New York, NY: Brentaro's Publishers, 1926).

[2] Herbert V. Prochnow, *The Public Speaker's Treasure Chest* (New York, NY: Harper & Bros. Publ., 1942).

Chapter 8

1   Lillian Eichler Watson, Edited and with Commentary by, *Lights From Many Lamps*, (New York, NY: Simon & Schuster, 1951).
2   Herbert V. Prochnow, *The Public Speaker's Treasure Chest*, (New York, NY: Harper & Bros., 1942).
3   Ibid, p. 326.

Chapter 9

1   Clinton T. Howell, ed., *Lines to Live By* (Nashville, TN: Thomas Nelson Publishers, 1972), p. 180

Chapter 11

1   Paul Lee Tan, ThD., *Encyclopedia of 7,700 Illustrations: Signs of the Times*, (Rockville, Maryland: Assurance Publishers, 1988).
2   Ignace Jan Paderewski and Mary Lawton, *The Paderewski Memoirs*, (New York, NY: C. Scribner's Sons, 1938).

Chapter 12

1   World Enclyclopedia, Vol. 3
2   Ibid., Vol. 14

Chapter 13

1   J. Cronin, *The Reader's Digest*, (The Turning Point of My Career), May 1941.

Chapter 14

1   William Eleazar Barton, *President Lincoln*, (Indianapolis, IN: Bobbs-Merrill, c. 1933).
2   Helen Keller, *The Story of My Life*, (New York, NY: Airmont Books, c. 1965).

Chapter 15

1 R.G. LeTourneau, *Mover of Men and Mountains*, (Chicago, IL: Moody Press, c. 1967).
2 Ibid., p. 126
3 Ibid., p. 265
4 Catherine Drinker, *Miracle at Philadelphia, The Story of the Constitutional Convention*, (Boston, MA: An Atlantic Monthly Press Book, c. 1966), pp. 125-126.
5 Tan, p. 158
6-9 Ibid.

Chapter 16

1 Herbert J. Gimpel, *Beethoven, Master Composer*, (New York, NY: Franklin Watts, Inc., c. 1970).
2 Ibid., p. 184
3 Keller, p. 59